KU-334-655

MARINE GYRO COMPASSES FOR SHIPS' OFFICERS

Marine Gyro Compasses for Ships' Officers

BY

A. FROST, B.Sc., Master Mariner, M.R.I.N.

GLASGOW

BROWN, SON & FERGUSON LTD. Nautical Publishers

4–10 Darnley Street

Copyright in all countries signatory to the Berne Convention

All rights reserved

First Edition 1982

ISBN 0 85174 426 5

© 1982 Brown, Son & Ferguson, Ltd.,
Glasgow G41 2SD

Printed and Made in Great Britain

D
673.86
FRO

CONTENTS

Introduction   The International System of Units. Linear and Angular Motion.   xi

Chapter 1

SECTION 1.1	The Free Gyroscope	1
1.2	Gyroscopic Inertia	2
1.3	The Free Gyro on the Rotating Earth	4
1.4	The Daily Motions of Stars	5
1.5	Formulae for Drifting and Tilting	9
1.6	Directions of Drifting and Tilting	10
1.7	Calculations on the Position and the Change of Position of the Spin Axis of a Free Gyro	12
1.8	Gyroscopic Precession. The Effect of External Forces on a Free Gyro	22
1.9	Rate of Precession	24
1.10	Control of the Free Gyro to Produce a North Seeking Instrument	24
1.11	To Show that the Control Precession is Proportional to the Tilt	27
1.12	The Effect of the Control Precession on the Free Gyroscope	29
1.13	The Effect of Latitude on the Controlled Ellipse	31
1.14	Control of the Gyro by Liquid Ballistic	32
1.15	Factors Influencing the Rate of Precession with a Liquid Ballistic	34
1.16	Damping the Controlled Ellipse	36
1.17	Damping in Tilt	36
1.18	To Show that the Damping Precession is Proportional to the Tilt	38
1.19	The Effect of the Damping Precession on the Controlled Ellipse	38
1.20	The Settling Position	40
1.21	Damping in Azimuth	42
1.22	The Damped Spiral for a Gyro Damped in Azimuth	45
1.23	The Settling Position	46
1.24	Latitude Error	47
1.25	Course Latitude and Speed Error	48
1.26	Formula for Course Latitude and Speed Error	50
1.27	The Change in the Course and Speed Error	52
1.28	The Effect of Ship Motions on the Gyro	52
1.29	The First Rolling Error	53
1.30	The Intercardinal Rolling Error	54
1.31	Elimination of The Intercardinal Rolling Error	57
1.32	Ballistic Deflection	59
1.33	Formula for Ballistic Deflection	60
1.34	Eliminating the Effects of Ballistic Deflection	60
1.35	Ballistic Deflection in Compasses not Schuler Tuned	62
1.36	Ballistic Tilt	63
1.37	The Directional Gyro	64

Chapter 2

Section 2.1	Sperry Gyro Compasses	66
2.2	The Sperry Mk. 20	66
2.3	Construction of the Mk. 20	66
2.4	The Phantom Ring	69
2.5	The Outer Member	69
2.6	Control of the Mk. 20	70
2.7	Damping of the Mk. 20	70
2.8	The Follow Up System	70
2.9	Action of the Compass when the Vessel Alters Course	72
2.10	The Gimbal Support	72
2.11	The Compass Card Assembly	74
2.12	The Binnacle	74
2.13	Correction of Errors	74
2.14	Error Correction Signals. The Correction Torque Motor	75
2.15	Transmission to Repeaters	78
2.16	The S.R. 120 Gyro Compass	79
2.17	The Sensitive Element	79
2.18	The Phantom Element	84
2.19	The Stationary Element	84
2.20	The Follow Up System	85
2.21	Error Correction	86
2.22	Transmission to Repeaters	87
2.23	The Mk. 37 Gyro Compass	92
2.24	Construction of the Mk. 37	92
2.25	Control of the Mk. 37	95
2.26	Damping of the Mk. 37	95
2.27	The Follow Up System	96
2.28	The Electronic Control Unit	97
2.29	The Transmission Unit	97
2.30	The Speed and Latitude Compensator Unit	97
2.31	Correction of Errors	97
2.32	Rapid Settling	98
2.33	Automatic Levelling	99
2.34	The Electrolytic Level	99

Chapter 3

Section 3.1	The Arma Brown Gyrocompass	101
3.2	The Sensitive Element	101
3.3	Connection of the Torsion Wires Between Tank and Ball	102
3.4	Purpose of the Torsion Wires	103
3.5	The Tank and its Supporting Gimbals	104
3.6	The Follow Up System	106
3.7	Control and Damping	108
3.8	The Pendulum Unit	109
3.9	The Use of the Pendulum Unit Signal	109
3.10	Correction of Errors	110
3.11	Correction of Latitude Error	110
3.12	Correction of Course Latitude and Speed Error	111

3.13 The Arma Brown as a Directional Gyro   113
3.14 Transmission to Repeaters   113
3.15 The Relay Transmitter   117
3.16 Synchro Transmission   117

Chapter 4

SECTION 4.1   The Anschutz Gyro Compasses   118
4.2   Construction of the Standard 4   118
4.3   The Twin Rotors   122
4.4   Control of the Standard 4   124
4.5   Damping of the Standard 4   124
4.6   The Follow Up System   124
4.7   Electrical Supply to the Gyrosphere   126
4.8   Error Correction   127
4.9   Elimination of Rolling Errors   127
4.10 The Standard 6   127
4.11 The Gyrosphere   128
4.12 The Outer Sphere   129
4.13 The Gimbal Support   129
4.14 The Compass Casing   130
4.15 The Standard 10   130
4.16 Construction of the Standard 10   130

Appendix

Alternating Currents   133

Electromagnetic Induction   134

Multi Phase Supplies   135

Induction Motors   135

Rotation of a Magnetic Field by Multi Phase Supplies   137

Synchro Transmission and Servo Mechanisms   140

PREFACE

Modern gyro compasses are reliable, often sealed units which require a minimum of attention from ship's officers, other than the normal starting and stopping routines. These tasks can be carried out without any knowledge of the principles upon which their operation depends. Unnecessary knowledge however is for the inquiring mind. A knowledge of gyro theory is necessary to properly appreciate the capabilities and the limitations of the compass, and the errors to which it is liable. The purpose of this handbook is to provide that knowledge while at the same time providing a text suitable for candidates for Department of Trade Class 1 and Class 3 certificates and for the Department of Trade Electronic Navigation Course.

Operating instructions for the compasses described are not included as these are invariably simple and straightforward and are provided by the manufacturers. General theory is described in the first chapter. Subsequent chapters show how this theory is used in the construction of practical gyro compasses in use currently in merchant vessels.

The author would like to thank Capt. W. Burger of the University of Wales Institute of Science and Technology, for his help and encouragement after reading the manuscript, and for his suggestions to improve the same.

ACKNOWLEDGEMENTS

The author acknowledges with thanks the cooperation and help from the following manufacturers of commercial gyro compasses:

Sperry Marine Systems,
   a division of The Sperry Rand Corporation.
Anschutz & Co. G.m.b.H. Kiel.
S. G. Brown Limited, a Hawker Siddeley Company.

Information concerning the Sperry Mk. 20, S.R. 120 and Mk. 37 compasses is published with the kind permission of Sperry Marine Systems. Figures 2.1(a), 2.3 and 2.7(c) and (d) are reproduced from Sperry manuals.

Information concerning the Anschutz Standards 4, 6, and 10 is published with the kind permission of Anschutz and Co. Figure 4.1(a) is reproduced from Anschutz manual

Information concerning the Arma Brown Compass is published with the kind permission of S. G. Brown Ltd. Figures 3.2(b), 3.3, 3.8, and 3.9 are reproduced from Arma Brown manuals.

INTRODUCTION

The International System of Units (S.I. Units)

All measurements are comparisons with some accepted standard. It is desirable that a common standard is adopted and to this end in 1960 the General Conference of Weights and Measures recommended that an internationally accepted system of units based upon the metric system should be universally adopted. This recommendation has now been widely implemented and the S.I. Units is briefly described here.

The International System of Units is based upon the kilogramme, the metre and the second, and there are six fundamental units defined. All other units are derived from, and defined in terms of these fundamental units. The three basic units of mass length and time, which are applicable to the work covered in this book are described. The other three basic units, the units of electrical current, temperature and luminous intensity have no application here and are not described.

MASS is an expression of the quantity of matter contained in a body. The unit of mass is the kilogramme (kg) which is arbitrarily defined by the mass of a sample of platinum-iridium alloy preserved at the International Office of Weights and Measures at Sevres in Paris. A convenient sub-unit is the gramme (kg $\times 10^{-3}$).

The fundamental unit of LENGTH is the metre, which, although the original intention was that it should be related to the length of a terrestrial meridian, is now arbitrarily defined in terms of the wavelength of a specified radiation of orange-red light from the atom of the gas Krypton-86. The use of physical standards provided by a length of metal rod has ceased to give a definition to the accuracy consistent with modern requirements and measurement techniques. Convenient sub-units are the centimetre (metre $\times 10^{-2}$), and the millimetre (metre $\times 10^{-3}$).

The fundamental unit of TIME is the second. This was originally defined in terms of the interval between astronomical events, and must necessarily be related to the length of the mean solar day. Observed variations in the length of this period now make such a definition inaccurate and the second is now defined in terms of the period of a specified radiation from the Caesium atom, and is measured by atomic clocks which are regulated to the behaviour of the earth in its axial rotation.

All units used in the following discussion are derived from and defined in terms of these three basic units.

Velocity

This is a rate of change of position. Position and velocity must be expressed relative to some fixed reference frame which is considered to have zero velocity. For measurements on the earth's surface this reference normally has zero velocity relative to the earth's surface, as this will then appear stationary to a terrestrial observer. The unit of velocity is the metre per second (m/s).

$$\text{velocity} = \frac{\text{distance moved}}{\text{time taken}}$$

Velocity is a vector quantity and as such must have a magnitude and a direction to define it.

Acceleration

This is a rate of change of velocity. The unit of acceleration is the metre per second per second (m/s^2).

$$\text{acceleration} = \frac{\text{change in velocity}}{\text{time taken}}$$

To define an acceleration the direction in which the change of velocity takes place must be specified.

Force

This is a push or a pull exerted on a mass. When a force acts on a mass an acceleration of the mass is produced which is proportional to the applied force. Force may be measured by this acceleration and the unit of force is defined as that force which when applied to a unit mass of 1 kg produces a unit acceleration of 1 m/s^2. This unit force is then called 1 Newton (*N*).

Thus

$$\text{force } (N) = \text{mass (kg)} \times \text{acceleration (m/s}^2)$$

or

$$F = ma.$$

Force is a vector quantity and therefore requires a direction and a magnitude.

Weight

There is a gravitational attraction between any two masses which tends to accelerate the masses towards each other. When either or both of the masses is large, as in the case of the earth and an object on its surface, or in the case of two astronomical bodies, the gravitational force is considerable. It is responsible for maintaining the orbital motions of bodies within the solar system and for the retention of the atmosphere around a planet. The gravitational force between two masses varies as the product of the masses and inversely as the square of their distance apart. This relationship is stated formally in Newton's law of universal gravitation:

$$F = G\frac{m_1 m_2}{d^2}$$

where G is the gravitational constant.

The attractive force which is exerted between the earth and a mass at the earth's surface is called the weight of that mass. The unit of weight is the unit of force the Newton and the weight of a mass is given by the product of its mass and the acceleration due to gravity (g), according to the law:

$$\text{force} = \text{mass} \times \text{acceleration}$$

$$\text{weight } (N) = \text{mass (kg)} \times g \text{ (m/s}^2)$$

Note that the mass of a body is constant, whereas its weight will vary due to any variations in the acceleration due to gravity. This will vary with position on the earth's surface and with height above the earth's surface. As the mass of a body is measured by its weight it is important that comparisons with standard masses are made under conditions of standard gravitational acceleration.

Inertia

This is a reluctance of a body to change its state of rest or uniform motion in a straight line. Newton's first law of motion states that an external force must act on a body for this to occur in order to overcome this inertia.

Momentum

The inertia of a body may be measured by its momentum which is the product of the mass and the velocity:

$$\text{momentum (kg m/s)} = \text{mass (kg)} \times \text{velocity (m/s)}.$$

Newton's second law of motion states that when a force acts on a body, the body suffers a change in its momentum which is proportional to the applied force. In practice, as the mass will remain constant, the change in the velocity, or acceleration, will be proportional to the force and it is from this relationship that the unit of force is derived and defined.

Angular Velocity

This is the rate at which the angle at the centre of rotation is swept out by the radius of a rotating body. It may be expressed in revolutions per minute or in degrees per second. The most convenient unit of angular velocity is usually the radian per second, this being denoted by the symbol (ω).

Since there are 2π radians in $360°$, then

$$1 \text{ r.p.m.} = \frac{2\pi}{60} \text{ rads/sec.}$$

Relationship between Angular Velocity and Linear Velocity

If a body rotates with an angular velocity of one revolution per second then:

$$\omega = 2\pi \text{ rads/sec.} = \frac{2\pi r}{r} \text{ rads/sec.}$$

The linear velocity of a point on the circumference of the rotating body of radius r will be the length of that circumference per second. Thus

$$v = 2\pi r \text{ m/s}$$

when r is expressed in metres and

$$\omega = \frac{v}{r} \text{ rads/sec.}$$

Angular Acceleration (ϕ)

This is a rate of change of angular velocity, and is given by:

$$\text{angular acceleration } (\phi) = \frac{\text{change of angular velocity}}{\text{time taken}}$$

The unit of angular acceleration is the radian per second per second.

Relationship between Angular Acceleration and Linear Acceleration

If

$$\text{angular acceleration} = \frac{\text{change of angular velocity}}{\text{time taken}}$$

$$= \frac{\omega_1 - \omega_2}{t}$$

and

$$\omega_1 = \frac{v_1}{r}$$

and

$$\omega_2 = \frac{v_2}{r}$$

$$= \frac{v_1 - v_2}{rt}$$

but

$$\frac{v_1 - v_2}{t}$$

is linear acceleration and therefore

$$\text{angular acceleration} = \frac{\text{linear acceleration}}{r}$$

or

$$\phi = \frac{a}{r}$$

Motion of Translation and Motion of Rotation

If a force acts on a mass which is unrestrained by any other forces, it will produce an acceleration along the direction in which the force acts. The mass will then have a rectilinear motion or a motion of pure translation in which all constituent particles of the mass are moving in the same direction at the same instantaneous velocity. There is one point associated with the mass called the centre of mass or centroid of the body, through which a force may act and produce only a motion of translation. If the force does not act through this point then a motion of rotation about the centre of mass will also be produced, and this requires that an angular acceleration be imparted to the mass. An angular acceleration is produced by a moment about the centre of mass.

A moment about a point is produced by a force which does not pass through that point. It is given by the product of the force and the perpendicular distance between the point and the line of action of the force:

$$\text{moment} (N - m) = \text{force} (N) \times \text{perpendicular distance} (m).$$

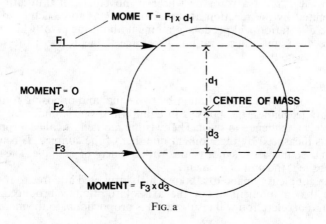

Fig. a

To Produce Pure Rotation of a Mass

In order to produce a motion of rotation but no motion of translation then the moment necessary for the rotational motion must be caused by a couple. This consists of two equal and opposite parallel forces whose resultant linear accelerations cancel but whose moments act in the same rotational sense. This is illustrated in figure b.

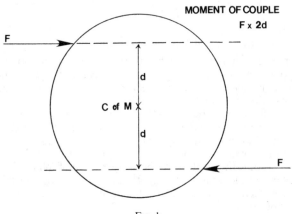

FIG. b

The moment produced by a couple is measured as the product of one of the forces and the perpendicular distance between their lines of action.

When a mass is pivoted about an axis through its centre of mass as in the case of a rotor or wheel, a movement of translation is prevented by the reaction at the pivot and any force acting in the plane of rotation will produce a moment about the pivot which will cause an angular acceleration. The force then produces the same effect as a couple.

Torque

If a body is being acted upon by two equal and opposing couples in parallel planes, the body is in equilibrium but is under torsion, which is a tendency to twist. The twisting moment is called a torque and is measured by the moment of either of the couples. Torque is often used in a sense synonymous with moment of a couple. The unit of torque is the unit of moment.

If a couple is applied to a body which is pivoted and free to rotate such that a moment about the axis of rotation is produced, an angular acceleration will result which is proportional to the moment of the applied couple. This is analogous to the production of a linear acceleration by a force.

Moment of Inertia

The inertia of a particle of a rotor requires a force in order to produce a linear acceleration of that particle. This force which must overcome the resistance to change, must be equal to the mass of the particle times the acceleration produced. Thus

$$\text{resistance of particle} = ma$$
$$= m\phi r.$$

The resistance to the rotation about a spin axis, due to this inertia, will be the moment of this force about that axis:

$$\text{moment} = m\phi r^2.$$

The total resistance to rotational motion due to the inertia of the whole rotor will be the sum of such expressions for each particle in the rotor:

$$\text{total resistance} = \phi\Sigma mr^2.$$

The quantity Σmr^2 is called the second moment of mass about the spin axis, or the moment of inertia about that axis, and as the total resistance moment must be opposed by any moment causing angular acceleration the moment of inertia will determine the acceleration caused by any given applied moment.

Radius of Gyration

The radius of gyration of a body with respect to a specified axis of rotation is that radius whose square when multiplied by the mass of the body gives the moment of inertia of the body about that axis. A rotating body therefore behaves as if the whole mass were considered to be concentrated at the radius of gyration.

It should be evident that the moment of inertia of a rotor depends upon the mass and its distribution relative to the axis of rotation. The greater is the radius of gyration the greater will be the moment of inertia, and the greater will be the moment necessary to produce a given angular acceleration. If a force or couple is applied to the rotor to produce a moment about the spin axis then an angular acceleration will result which is proportional to the applied moment. The constant of proportionality is the moment of inertia of the rotor about the spin axis. Thus

$$T = I\phi$$

where T = moment of applied couple
             I = moment of inertia about the spin axis
             ϕ = angular acceleration.

To Find the Moment of Inertia of a Rotor of Rectangular Cross Section, About its Axis of Rotation

The moment of inertia of a particle of mass, m, about an axis distance r from the particle is given by:

$$mr^2.$$

Consider a thin cylindrical ring of incremental radius δr, from the rotor as illustrated in figure c.

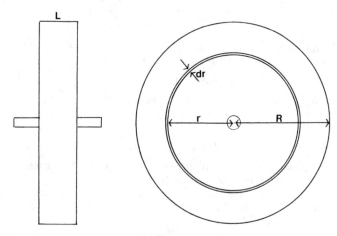

F$_{IG}$. c

The volume of this ring is $2\pi r \delta r L$, the mass is $2\pi r \delta r L \rho$.
Moment of Inertia about the axis of rotation is given by:

$$\text{mass} \times r^2 = 2\pi r \delta r L \rho r^2$$

$$= 2\pi \rho L r^3 \delta r.$$

For the whole rotor, the moment of inertia is found by integrating this expression over the range of radii from 0 to R:

$$= 2\pi \rho L \int_0^R r^3 \, dr$$

$$= 2\pi \rho L \left[\frac{r^4}{4} \right]_0^R$$

$$= \frac{2\pi \rho L R^4}{4}$$

$$= \frac{\pi \rho L R^4}{2}$$

but

$$\text{mass} = \pi R^2 L \rho$$

$$\text{M. of I.} = \frac{\text{mass} \times R^2}{2} = \frac{MR^2}{2}.$$

Angular Momentum

An elemental particle of a rotor at any instant will have a linear momentum along the tangent equal to its mass times its linear velocity.

As

$$v = \omega r$$

then

$$\text{linear momentum} = m\omega r.$$

The moment of this momentum about the axis of rotation is found by multiplying by the radius r.

Thus moment of momentum or angular momentum $= m\omega r^2$.

The total angular momentum of the rotor is therefore the sum of such expressions for all the elemental particles

$$= \Sigma m\omega r^2$$

$$= \omega I.$$

Thus the angular momentum of a rotor is equal to the product of its angular velocity and its moment of inertia about the axis of rotation.

CHAPTER 1

GYROSCOPIC COMPASS THEORY

1.1 Introduction—The Gyroscope

A gyroscope consists of a mass in the form of a rotor or wheel which is suspended in such a way that it is free to spin about an axis passing through its centre of mass and perpendicular to the plane of the rotor. This axis is referred to as the spin axis. Ideally the spin axis bearings should be frictionless so that any rotation imparted to the rotor is maintained.

If the gyroscope is not constrained in any way so that there are no forces acting upon the rotor so as to alter the direction in which the spin axis points, then the gyro is called a free gyroscope. The best example of a free gyroscope is the earth itself or indeed any astronomical body which is rotating about one of its diameters, as is the earth. Such bodies are freely suspended in space and if we disregard the small gravitational forces arising from the presence of other astronomical bodies, then the spinning earth may be considered to be free from any external forces which act to change the direction in which its spin axis points. The earth therefore exhibits the properties of a free gyroscope, the equatorial mass corresponding to the plane of the rotor and the earth's axis of rotation constituting the spin axis.

In order to construct a free gyroscope on the surface of the earth then the rotor must be supported against the effect of the earth's gravity. The supports must be designed to maintain the freedom of the spin axis of the rotor to take up any direction without constraint. This requires a gimbal mounting which gives the rotor freedom to turn about two axes mutually at right angles and at right angles to the spin axis. It is convenient to adopt the vertical axis, and a horizontal axis mutually at right angles to the spin axis and the vertical axis. The gyro therefore will have freedom to tilt about the horizontal axis and to turn in azimuth about the vertical axis. Friction in the bearings of the gimbal mountings should be negligible to avoid applying torques to the rotor.

A free gyro therefore is said to have three degrees of freedom:

    i. freedom to spin about a spin axis.
   ii. freedom to turn in azimuth about a vertical axis.
  iii. freedom to tilt about a horizontal axis.

Figure 1.1 shows an arrangement of such a free gyroscope.

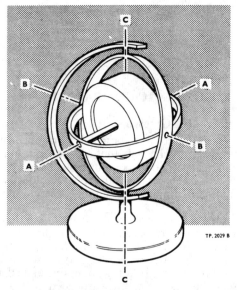

Fig. 1.1   An arrangement of gimbals to give a rotor freedom to tilt and to turn in azimuth.

AA = Spin axis.
BB = Horizontal axis.
CC = Vertical axis.

If such a rotor is caused to rotate about its spin axis with a relatively high angular velocity, the free gyroscope will exhibit the property of Gyroscopic Inertia, or Rigidity in Space.

1.2   Gyroscopic Inertia

When the rotor of a free gyroscope is spinning the forces which are acting upon an elemental particle of the rotor are those of centrifugal force, which is directed radially outwards, and an equal and opposing force which is directed radially inwards. This opposing force is provided by the cohesion of the particles in the solid rotor. Both these forces are acting in directions which are in the plane of the rotor and therefore do not act to change the plane in which the rotor is orientated. If the friction in the spin axis bearings is neglected the rotor will continue to spin with a constant velocity and will maintain the orientation of the plane of the rotor in space. The spin axis will therefore point to a constant direction with respect to space, and it is this property which is known as gyroscopic inertia or rigidity in space.

The gyroscopic inertia of a rotor may be expressed quantitatively by its angular momentum (H). This will determine how much force is necessary to change the direction in which the spin axis points at a given rate. The angular momentum depends upon:

  a. the angular velocity of the rotor (ω),
  b. the moments of inertia of the cross section about the spin axis (I).

The moment of inertia of the cross section expresses the moment that the mass of the rotor exerts about the spin axis, that is the axis of gyration of the rotor. This will determine how easy it is to initially set the rotor spinning or to increase or decrease the angular velocity when it is spinning, that is to change its state of motion. The moment of inertia will depend upon the mass of the rotor, and also upon the distribution of that mass with respect to the spin axis. The greater the proportion of the mass which lies towards the circumference of the rotor then the greater will be the moment of inertia and the greater will be the gyroscopic inertia for any given angular velocity. Rotors are for this reason designed with a heavy rim with a relatively light internal construction which is only sufficient to maintain the strength of the rotor. Figure 1.2 shows the cross sections of two rotors. The

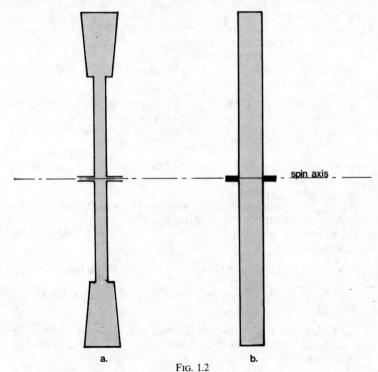

a.   b.

FIG. 1.2

moment of inertia of the cross section of rotor a will be greater than that of rotor b. Rotor a will therefore possess greater gyroscopic inertia for any given angular velocity of spin.

Angular momentum (H), is given by the product of the angular velocity (ω), and the moment of inertia of the cross section about the spin axis (I):

$$H = \omega I.$$

1.3   The Free Gyroscope on the Rotating Earth

It must be stressed that the orientation of the plane of the rotor is constant with respect to space, and that this direction will apparently change when considered with respect to the surface of the rotating earth. Any star in the heavens is at such a vast distance from the earth that its motion through space has a negligible effect upon its position with respect to the other stars, and the familiar star constellation patterns are maintained. A star therefore may be considered as lying in a constant direction in space. It is convenient to consider the spin axis of a free gyro as pointing to a star, imaginary or otherwise, which is referred to as the gyro star. Motions of the spin axis relative to the earth's surface may then be understood by considering the daily motion of the gyro star. This is a subject with which the navigator is familiar.

The direction in which the gyro axis points relative to the earth's surface may be expressed by:

   i. The Tilt: This is the angle of elevation or depression of the spin axis above or below the horizontal.
   ii. The Azimuth: This is the direction in which the spin axis points relative to the direction of true north.

By convention the tilt and the azimuth of that end of the spin axis which is directed towards the north is stated and used in all discussion of gyro theory.

The tilt and the azimuth of the gyro spin axis is equivalent to the altitude and azimuth (bearing) of the gyro star.

The movement of the spin axis relative to the earth's surface may be expressed by:

   i. The Tilting: This is the rate of change of the tilt of the spin axis.
   ii. The Drifting: This is the rate of change of the azimuth of the spin axis.

The tilting and the drifting of the spin axis are equivalent to the rate of change of altitude and the rate of change of azimuth (bearing) of the gyro star.

1.4 Daily Motion of the Stars

Here it may be advantageous to consider the apparent motions of the stars, resulting from the daily rotation of the earth about its own spin axis.

The earth rotates about an axis through its poles once in 23h 56m 4·09s of solar time. This period is called a sidereal day and may be subdivided into 24 sidereal hours. In the following discussion any reference to time will assume sidereal time, and as the sidereal day may be taken to be the interval required for a 360° rotation of the earth, the rate of rotation may be expressed as 15° per hour, or as 15 minutes of arc per minute of time, whichever is convenient.

The west to east rotation of the earth is apparent to an observer on the earth's surface as an east to west rotation of the celestial concave about an axis which is coincident with the earth's axis. It is convenient therefore to consider the earth as stationary and the celestial sphere to rotate in the opposite direction. As the axis of rotation of the heavens defines the celestial poles, all points on the sphere will appear to describe circular paths around the poles, which will be the only points on the sphere which do not appear to move relative to the earth's surface. The complete circle described by the star in the sidereal day will sometimes lie completely above the observer's horizon and sometimes will lie partially below the horizon. Whether the star sets or not will depend upon which is greater, the observer's latitude or the stars angular distance from the pole.

Consider an observer situated at one of the earth's poles, say the north pole. The north celestial pole will lie at the observer's zenith, the point in the sky directly above him. The rotation of the stars about the pole will also be therefore about the zenith. All stars will describe a circle parallel to the horizon, maintaining a constant altitude. (This altitude will be equal to the stars declination.) There will be no rising or setting phenomena. These conditions are illustrated in figure 1.3.

The spin axis of a free gyro at the pole will maintain a constant tilt while drifting westwards around the horizon at a rate equal to the earth's rotation, that is 15° per hour. A gyro set with its spin axis directed towards the zenith, that is with a tilt of 90° is pointing at the celestial pole. It would therefore continue to point in the same direction as the pole marks a constant direction in space which has no apparent motion relative to the earth's surface.

Consider now an observer at the equator. His zenith will lie on the equinoctial or celestial equator and the north celestial pole must lie on the horizon bearing north. This is illustrated in figure 1.4.

As the axis of rotation now lies in the plane of the observer's horizon, the rotation must carry all celestial bodies above and below the horizon for equal periods of time. Furthermore all circles of declination cut the horizon in a right angle, so that any body will, at

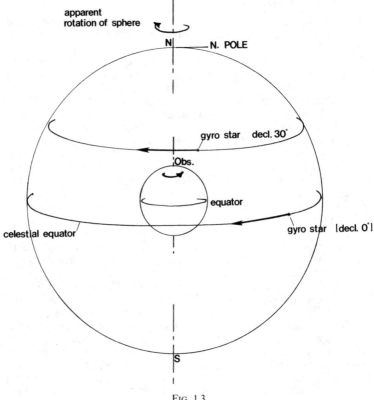

FIG. 1.3

the moment of rising be moving perpendicularly to the horizon. It will then spend 12 hours above the horizon before setting at which time it will again be moving perpendicularly to the horizon.

The point at which a star crosses the horizon is determined by the star's declination. A star with declination zero, that is a star which lies on the celestial equator, will rise bearing due east, will pass through the zenith, and will set bearing due west. The rate of change of altitude will be equal to the rate of the earth's rotation, 15° per hour. Consider the motion of the spin axis of the free gyro at the equator, assuming that it is set initially pointing due east and horizontal. It is pointing at the gyro star of zero declination which is rising. The spin axis will tilt upwards at the rate of 15° per hour (i.e. tilting = 15° per hour), but the drifting is zero. The azimuth will remain 090° until the spin axis is directed towards the zenith. Thereafter the azimuth will be 270° with the tilting −15° per hour,

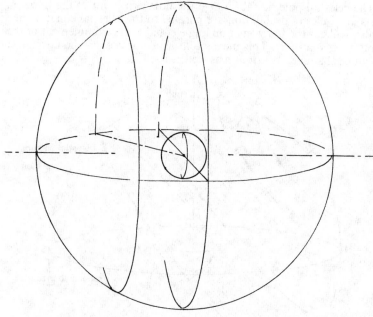

FIG. 1.4

the axis again becoming horizontal as the gyro sets bearing due west.

A star situated at the celestial pole would have no motion relative to the earth's surface. A gyro spin axis which is set pointing north and horizontal would therefore remain so. Drifting and tilting would be zero.

A star with a declination other than zero or 90° would cross the horizon perpendicularly with an amplitude equal to the declination. The star would rise to a maximum altitude equal to its polar distance as it crosses the meridian. The azimuth will change during its passage across the sky but at the moment of rising or setting the rate of change of azimuth would be zero. A gyro spin axis which is set horizontal therefore will have zero drifting irrespective of its azimuth. In general drifting may be taken as zero at the equator as long as the tilt is small. As a gyro compass never attains a large tilt this assumption is a reasonable approximation. The rate of tilting will vary as the sine of the azimuth.

Consider now an observer in an intermediate northerly latitude. The zenith will lie between the celestial pole and the celestial equator. Figure 1.5 illustrates an observer in latitude 40°N.

The plane of the celestial equator is inclined to the observer's vertical by 40° and will therefore cut the horizon at an angle of 50°.

The celestial pole lies 40° above the northern point of the horizon. As all circles of declination are parallel to the celestial equator they also will cut the horizon at an angle equal to the complement of the observer's latitude. This means that as a star crosses the horizon it will be changing its azimuth as well as its altitude.

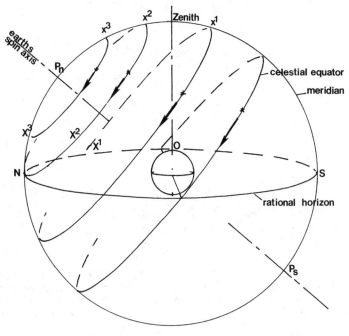

Fig. 1.5

In figure 1.5 three circles of declination are shown. Star X_1 has declination same name as the latitude and less than the latitude. At rising (at X_1) the azimuth will be increasing and will continue to do so until the star crosses the meridian at x_1, south of the observer's zenith. Star X_2 has declination greater than the latitude and will cross the meridian to the north of the zenith, at x_2. Star X_3 is circumpolar, that is it does not set below the horizon to an observer in this latitude.

A gyro spin axis will, if its projection onto the celestial sphere is considered, trace out such circular paths around the pole. The radius of the circle traced out will depend upon where the spin axis is initially pointing. If the axis is set horizontal and directed towards X_1 to the east of the meridian, then it will trace out the circular path associated with the star X_1. If the spin axis is set pointing north and

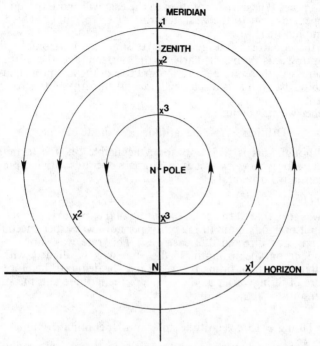

FIG. 1.6

tilted upwards to point towards X_3 then the circle traced out will be that associated with the circumpolar star X_3.

It is sometimes convenient to show these circular paths as seen by an observer facing the northern horizon. Figure 1.6 shows the northern horizon and the meridian passing through its northern point. The pole is seen above the horizon bearing north with an altitude equal to the observer's latitude. The circular paths referred to in figure 1.5 are shown and labelled accordingly. Note that the stars will be seen to move anticlockwise rising to the east of the pole and setting when to the west of the pole.

1.5   Formulae for Drifting and Tilting

From the discussion of the apparent daily motions of stars in section 1.4 we may deduce simple formulae for the Drifting and the Tilting of a free gyro.

Drifting (Dg)

We have seen that the drifting of a free gyro spin axis is equal to the rate of the earth's rotation for a free gyro placed at either of the earth's poles. The earth's rotation to the east will cause the spin axis to appear to drift to the west at a rate of 15° per hour. This is the maximum rate.

At the equator a free gyro with its spin axis horizontal will be tilting upwards perpendicularly to the horizon, and the drifting at this time will therefore be zero irrespective of the azimuth. Thus for a gyro whose spin axis has a negligible tilt the drifting is zero at the equator.

Hence we may deduce:

Drifting = 15′ sine latitude per minute of time.

(Although this is true only for a negligible tilt, the formula is adequate for gyro work as a gyro compass operates with its spin axis substantially horizontal.)

Tilting (Tg)

It was seen that at the poles the tilting of the spin axis was zero. At the equator a maximum tilting of 15° per hour was experienced if the spin axis was directed due east/west. This rate was shown to be dependent on the azimuth. If the spin axis is aligned with the meridian the rate of tilting is zero. It may be deduced therefore that the rate of tilting varies as the cosine of the latitude and the sine of the azimuth.

Hence:

Tilting = 15′ cos latitude sin azimuth per minute of time.

The foregoing does not constitute strict mathematical proof of the formulae but the discussion may help the student to remember or to think out the formulae for himself.

1.6 Direction of Drifting and Tilting

It is most important that the student is able to determine the direction of the drifting and the tilting, from any given initial azimuth and tilt. This may be determined by considering figure 1.7 which shows the circular path traced out by a star during a sidereal day, around the north celestial pole, as seen by an observer facing the northern horizon. The plane of the page is representing the curved surface of the celestial sphere, and the north celestial pole has an altitude above the horizon equal to the observer's latitude. The star will circle the pole in the direction shown, that is increasing its altitude when it is to the east of the meridian, crossing the meridian above the pole, and decreasing its altitude when to the west of the meridian.

This is the path traced out by the projection of the north end of the spin axis of a free gyro which is initially set pointing in the direction X. From the figure we may deduce that, when the north end of the axis is directed to the east of the meridian, that end will be

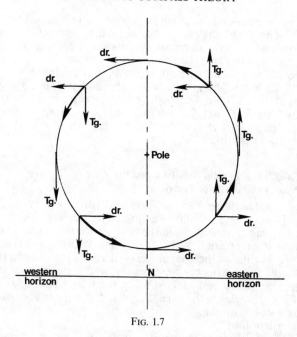

Fig. 1.7

increasing its tilt, that is the tilting will be positive. When the north end is directed to the west of the meridian that end will decrease its tilt, that is tilting will be negative. Similarly we may deduce that when the north end of the axis is directed below the north pole that end will drift to the east, that is drifting will be positive. When the north end of the axis is directed above the pole that end will drift to the west, that is drifting will be negative. The tilting will be zero when the spin axis is aligned with the meridian, and the drifting will be zero when the tilt of the axis is equal to the altitude of the pole, which is equal to the observer's latitude.

The sign convention introduced in the foregoing discussion may be summarised thus:

North end of spin axis drifting eastwards   Dg. +ve.
    (clockwise)
North end of spin axis drifting westwards   Dg. −ve.
    (anticlockwise)

North end of spin axis tilting upwards   Tg. +ve.
North end of spin axis tilting downwards   Tg. −ve.

By convention the sign applied to the drifting and the tilting describes the movement of that end of the spin axis which is directed towards the north.

A gyro compass operates with a zero or a very small tilt. As the altitude of the celestial pole is equal to the observer's latitude, in north latitude the gyro compass spin axis will operate always with the north end directed below the north pole. The drifting will therefore always be eastwards or positive. In south latitude the north pole will be below the northern horizon and the spin axis will be directed above the pole. The drifting will therefore be westwards. We may say therefore that for a gyro compass in north latitude the drifting is eastwards or positive, and in south latitude the drifting is westwards or negative.

1.7   Calculations on the Position and the Rate of Change of Position of the Spin Axis of a Free Gyro

The formulae derived for drifting and tilting give values which are valid only for an instant in time. The value given for tilting depends upon the value used in the formula for the azimuth and this will be constantly changing. The formula for drifting is valid only for a zero tilt. The use of these formulae is therefore limited and they are not suitable for use in problems covering a long interval of time. These problems are best tackled using the trigonometrical solution of the PZX triangle for the gyro star, which problems are familiar to the navigator who has studied the principles of navigation or nautical astronomy.

To illustrate these problems it is usual to draw an approximate projection of the celestial sphere onto the rational horizon based upon the equidistant projection. Accurate scale drawing of such figures is not necessary but the general procedure for figure drawing is given here. Procedure is referred to figure 1.8.

1. Describe a circle to represent the rational horizon. The view of the celestial sphere is from above the observer's zenith so that the centre of the circle will always represent the zenith. This is labelled Z. The north point of the horizon is marked by N and the south point by S.

2. Draw in the line NZS to represent the observer's meridian. This divides the sphere into two halves, east of the meridian in which all bodies rise, and west of the meridian in which all bodies set. Draw in WZE to represent the observer's prime vertical.

3. Mark an approximate scale of degrees along NZS in say 10° intervals. This scale may be used as a scale of latitude, declination or altitude.

4. Mark in the point Q where the celestial equator cuts the meridian. The distance ZQ will be equal to the observer's latitude. Q will be to the south of Z if the latitude is north, and Q will be to the north of Z if the latitude is south. Draw an arc through W, Q and E to represent the celestial equator.

5. Now locate some point which is occupied by the gyro star at

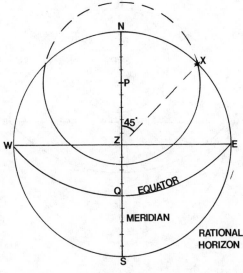

FIG. 1.8

some instant, from information given in the question. For example it may be given that initially the gyro axis is horizontal and pointing in a direction 045°. This would locate the gyro star on the horizon at X in figure 9.8. The examples worked in the following section will illustrate this further.

6. For the present purpose it is now sufficiently accurate to draw a circle centred upon P through the gyro star so located. This circle represents the path followed by the gyro star during the daily rotation of the earth.

The following examples worked with notes will now show how such a figure may be used to solve this type of problem.

Example 1

A free gyro in latitude 40°N is initially set pointing north with its spin axis horizontal. Find the position of the north end of the spin axis 12 hours later.

Notes

A diagram may first be drawn for 40° north latitude. The gyro star is then initially positioned on the horizon (gyro axis horizontal), and bearing north. The gyro star is therefore initially at N in figure 1.9. The circle drawn about P passing through N then represents the path traced out by spin axis during one rotation of the earth. In 12 sidereal hours the spin axis will have traced out 180° of this

B

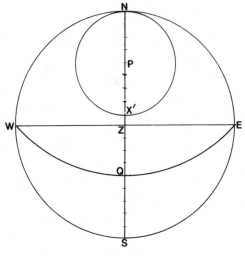

Fig. 1.9

diurnal circle, so that being initially on the lower meridian, the gyro star will then be on the upper meridian at X'.

In figure 9.9 observer's latitude = ZQ = PN = altitude of pole. Polar distance of gyro star = PN = PX' = 40°.

Thus

$$ZX' = 90° - 40° - 40° = 10°$$

and

$$\text{altitude} = 90° - ZX' = 80°.$$

Answer: *Gyro axis has tilt of + 80° pointing north.*

Example 2

A free gyro in latitude 50°N is initially set with its spin axis horizontal and pointing 030°. Find the interval of time elapsed before the gyro is pointing in the meridian, and before the gyro axis is again horizontal.

Notes

A diagram for 50°N may first be drawn. The gyro star may initially be positioned on the horizon (gyro axis horizontal), and bearing 030°. This is shown at X in figure 1.10. Draw a circle centred on P passing through X. This will represent the path traced out by the gyro spin axis during the one rotation of the earth.

The time taken for the gyro star to reach the meridian may be found by solving the triangle PZX to find angle P. This is the change

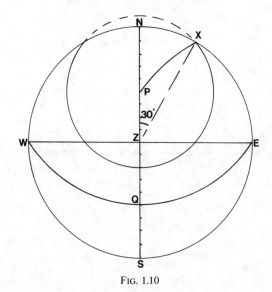

Fig. 1.10

of hour angle of the gyro star between crossing the horizon and crossing the meridian. Hour angle is changed by 15° per sidereal hour.

In figure 1.10 solving triangle PZX by Napier's rules:

$$\text{Sin comp. } PZ = -\text{Tan } Z \text{ Tan comp } P$$
$$-\text{Cot } P = \text{Cos } PZ \text{ Cot } Z$$
$$= \text{Cos } 40° \text{ Cot } 30°$$
$$P = -37° \, 00\cdot3' \text{ (second quadrant)}$$
$$P = 142° \, 59\cdot7'$$
$$\text{Time interval} = \frac{142° \, 59\cdot7'}{15}$$
$$= 9 \text{ hrs. } 32 \text{ mins.}$$

Note

The interval elapsed before the spin axis is again horizontal will now be twice this interval, as this will occur when the gyro star is at X′ in figure 1.10.

Thus answers = *time to reach meridian—9 hrs. 32 mins.*
                time to reach horizontal—19 hrs. 4 mins.

Example 3

A free gyro in latitude 52°N is initially set with its spin axis horizontal and with one end pointing 050°. Find the tilt of that end of the axis and its direction when it is in the meridian.

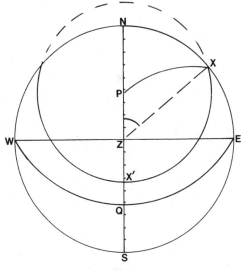

Fig. 1.11

Note

Figure 1.11 illustrates the problem, the initial conditions of which are similar to those of example 2. From the figure however it is evident that the star will pass to the south of the zenith, whereas in example 2 the star passed to the north. This will depend upon which is the greater, the latitude or the declination of the gyro star. Remember that the figures drawn are approximate and to determine definitely whether the star will pass to the north or the south, the declination must be calculated by solving the PZX triangle for PX, the polar distance. Declination is then 90°−polar distance.

This will determine whether the end of the spin axis originally considered will point north or south when it is in the meridian, and also will enable the tilt of the axis (altitude of the gyro star) to be found at this time.

From figure 1.11. In triangle PZX:

$$ZX = 90°.$$

By Napier's rules

$$\text{Sin comp. PX} = \text{Cos comp. PZ Cos Z}$$
$$\text{Cos PX} = \text{Sin PZ Cos Z}$$
$$= \text{Sin } 38° \text{ Cos } 50°$$
$$\text{PX} = 66° \ 41·3'.$$

Thus declination $= 90° - 66° \ 41·3'$
$$= 23° \ 18·7'\text{N}.$$

Gyro star will pass to the south of the observer.

$$\begin{aligned}
\text{Altitude of gyro star} &= 90° - ZX' \\
&= 90° - (QZ - QX') \\
&= 90° - (52° - 23° 18 \cdot 7') \\
&= 61° 18 \cdot 7'.
\end{aligned}$$

Answer: *Gyro axis will point south with a tilt of* $+61°$ 18.7′.

Example 4

A free gyro in latitude 45°N is initially set with its spin axis horizontal with end pointing north. Find the tilt and azimuth of that end after 6, 12 and 18 sidereal hours.

Notes

Figure 1.12 illustrates this problem. The gyro star is initially positioned on the horizon (gyro spin axis horizontal) at N. The circle drawn centred on P passing through N, also passes through the observer's zenith. This is because the latitude is 45° and PN = PZ, this being equal to the declination of the gyro star (also the polar distance). After 12 sidereal hours therefore the gyro star will be at Z, that is the spin axis of the gyro will point vertically upwards. After 6 sidereal hours the tilt and azimuth of the axis must be found by solving the PZX triangle shown in figure 1.12. In six sidereal hours the hour angle will have changed by 90°. Thus the angle P in the PZX triangle is 90°.

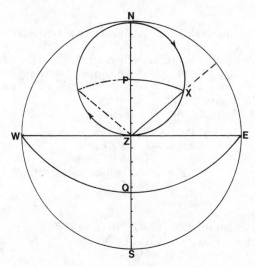

FIG. 1.12

In PZX triangle by Napier's rules:

$$\text{Sin comp. } ZX = \text{Cos } PZ \text{ Cos } PX$$
$$\text{Cos } ZX = \text{Cos } 45° \text{ Cos } 45°$$
$$= 0\cdot 5$$
$$ZX = 60°$$
$$\text{altitude} = 30°$$

and

$$\text{Sin } PZ = \text{Tan } PX \text{ Tan comp. } Z.$$
$$\text{Cot } Z = \text{Sin } PZ \text{ Cot } PX$$
$$= \text{Sin } 45° \text{ Cot } 45°$$
$$= 0\cdot 7071$$
$$Z = 54° \ 44\cdot 1'.$$

These calculations are also valid for the PZX triangle shown dashed in figure 1.12 applicable to the gyro star after 18 sidereal hours. Thus we may state the answers.

Answers: *After six hours tilt* $= 30°$, *pointing* $N54° \ 44\cdot 1' E$
                After twelve hours tilt $= 90°$
                After eighteen hours tilt $= 30°$, *pointing* $N54° \ 44\cdot 1' W.$

Example 5

A free gyro in latitude 25°S is set initially with its spin axis horizontal with one end pointing S 40° E. Find the tilt of that end after a period of six hours.

Notes

Figure 1.13 illustrates this problem. The gyro star is initially positioned at X^1. In six hours the hour angle will change by 90°. This problem requires the solution of two triangles, PZX^1 and PZX^2. First solve PZX^1 to find angle P. The angle P in triangle PZX^2 will then be found by taking 90° from it. Triangle PZX^2 can then be solved for ZX to give the tilt.

In PZX^1 by Napier's rules

$$\text{Sin comp. } PZ = -\text{Tan } Z \text{ Tan comp. } P$$
$$\text{Cot } P = -\text{Cos } PZ \text{ Cot } Z$$
$$= -\text{Cos } 65° \text{ Cot } 40°$$
$$P = -63° \ 16' \text{ (second quadrant)}$$
$$P = 116° \ 44'$$

and

$$\text{Sin comp. } PX = \text{Cos } Z \text{ Cos comp. } PZ$$
$$\text{Cos } PX = \text{Cos } 40° \text{ Sin } 65°$$
$$PX = 46° \ 01\cdot 8'.$$

Thus in triangle PZX^2:

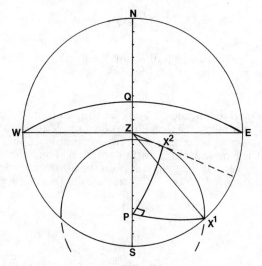

FIG. 1.13

$$\text{angle P} = 116° \, 44' - 90°$$
$$= 26° \, 44'$$

by spherical haversine formula:

$$\text{Hav ZX} = (\text{hav P sin PZ sin PX}) + \text{hav(PZ} \sim \text{PX)}$$
$$= (\text{hav } 26° \, 44' \sin 65° \sin 46° \, 01.8') + \text{hav } 18° \, 58.2'$$

Number	log.
hav 26° 44′	$\bar{2}$·72791
sin 65°	$\bar{1}$·95728
sin 46° 1·8′	$\bar{1}$·85715
	$\bar{2}$·54234
	0·03486
hav 18° 58·2′	0·02716
hav ZX	0·06202

$$\text{ZX} = 28° \, 50·4'.$$

Answer: *Tilt (altitude of gyro star)* = 61° 09·6′.

Example 6

A free gyro in latitude 0° is set initially with its spin axis horizontal and with one end pointing

a, north,
b, 045°,
c, 090°.

In each case find in which direction the north end of the spin axis will point in six hours, and the tilt.

Notes

With the gyro in latitude 0°, the poles will lie on the horizon. If the spin axis is pointing north then it must be directed towards the north celestial pole, in which case it will remain pointing in that direction throughout the period of the earth's rotation. Thus after six hours the tilt will be zero. If the gyro star is on the horizon bearing 045° as in part b, the angle P in the PZX triangle shown in figure 1.14, will

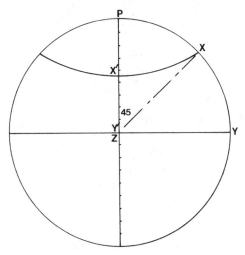

Fig. 1.14

be 90°. This will also be the case in part c with the gyro star bearing 090°. In both cases therefore after six hours the gyro star will be on the meridian, and the axis will point north–south. In part b the tilt will be 45°, and in part c the tilt will be 90° as the axis will point to the zenith. In the case of part c the declination of the gyro star is zero and its circle of declination will coincide with the celestial equator. No calculations are required to solve this problem if the student has mastered the principles of the previous problems.

Example 7

A free gyro in latitude 60°N is initially set with one end of its spin axis pointing 072° and tilted 20° above the horizontal. Determine the tilt when the axis is in the meridian and the direction when the axis is next horizontal.

Notes

There is no right angle in the initial PZX triangle so that a solution by the spherical haversine formula is necessary. Solve for PX to find the declination of the gyro star. This will enable the altitude when on the meridian to be found. A solution of a second PZX triangle when the gyro star sets will give Z the aximuth at that time. This can be done by Napier's rules as the side ZX will be 90° at setting.

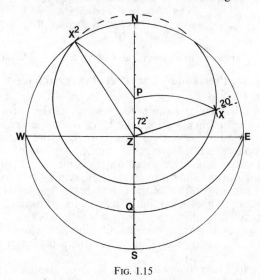

FIG. 1.15

In figure 1.15. In triangle PZX by spherical haversine formula

$$\text{Hav PX} = (\text{hav Z sin PZ sin ZX}) + \text{hav}(\text{PZ} \sim \text{ZX})$$
$$= (\text{hav } 72° \sin 30° \sin 70°) + \text{hav } 40°.$$

Number	log.
hav 72°	$\bar{1}\cdot53844$
sin 30°	$\bar{1}\cdot69897$
sin 70°	$\bar{1}\cdot97299$
	$\bar{1}\cdot21040$
	$0\cdot16233$
hav 40°	$0\cdot11698$
hav PX	$0\cdot27931$

$$PX = 63° 48·5'$$
$$\text{declination} = 26° 11·5'$$

Zenith distance of gyro star on meridian $= \text{lat.} - \text{dec.}$
$$= 60° - 26° 11·5'$$
$$= 33° 48·5'$$
$$\text{altitude} = 56° 11·5' \text{ bearing south.}$$

Answer: *Tilt when in meridian* $= 56° 11·5'$

and in triangle PZX^2 by Napier's rules

$$\text{Sin comp. } PX = \cos Z \cos \text{comp. } PZ$$
$$\cos Z = \cos PX \operatorname{cosec} PZ$$
$$= \cos 63° 48·5' \operatorname{cosec} 30°$$
$$Z = 28° 01·4'.$$

Answer: *Azimuth when gyro is next horizontal*—$N\ 28° 01·4'W$.

1.8   Gyroscopic Precession—The effect of external forces acting on a gyro

Any external force or couple which acts on the rotor may be resolved into components about the three axes, the spin axis, the horizontal axis, and the vertical axis. It is therefore convenient to consider couples about these axes separately.

A couple producing a torque about the spin axis acting in the plane of the rotor, as shown in figure 1.16, will merely increase or decrease the rate of rotation of the rotor about the spin axis. In this category is the drag of frictional forces in the spin axis bearings, which will decelerate the rotor. A torque which acts so as to oppose friction and thus maintain a constant angular velocity must be provided in a gyro compass. This will be the function of the rotor motor.

A couple which acts in a plane which is perpendicular to the plane of the rotor will contain a zero component about the spin axis. Such a couple may be resolved into components about the vertical and the

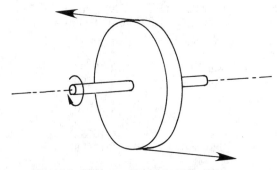

Fig. 1.16   Torques acting in the plane of the rotor.

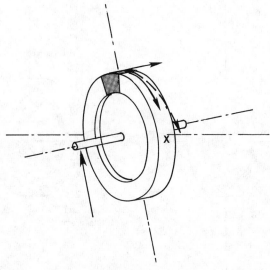

FIG. 1.17

horizontal axes. Figure 1.17 shows a rotor with a couple acting in a plane perpendicular to the rotor plane such as to cause a torque about the horizontal axis. (Apparently the effect of this torque is to produce a tilting of the spin axis, north end down and south end up.) The element of the rotor which is shaded however must move in a direction which is the resultant of its angular velocity about the spin axis and the motion imparted to it by the external couple. It will therefore move in the direction indicated by the dashed line in figure 1.17. It must eventually arrive at a point displaced in azimuth from the point X, which means that the spin axis must rotate about the vertical axis, a movement in azimuth.

We must state an important conclusion therefore that a couple acting perpendicularly on the plane of the rotor about a horizontal axis will produce a rotation of the spin axis about the vertical axis, and vice versa. In order to determine the effect of a force acting onto the plane of the rotor we must mentally carry the point of application of the force around the rotor through 90° in the direction of spin. The rotor will now turn, or precess, as if the force were acting at this displaced point.

Figure 1.18 shows a rotor with a couple acting in the vertical plane, about the horizontal axis. This is equivalent to an application of a force on the rotor at F. If F is now carried around through 90° in the direction of spin it will arrive at F'. This indicates that the rotor will precess about the vertical axis, the north end moving to the west and the south end to the east. Similarly in figure 1.18b the

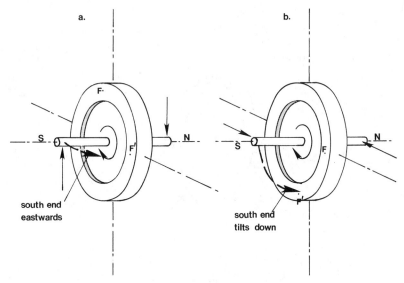

Fig. 1.18   Showing the direction of precession.

couple acting about the vertical axis, is equivalent to the application of a force on the rotor at F, which after being moved through 90° in the direction of spin arrives at F'. The rotor will therefore tilt or precess about the horizontal axis. The student should seek an opportunity to experience and verify this by experiment for himself.

1.9   Rate of Precession

The rate of precession of the gyro axis is proportional to the applied torque. It is also inversely proportional to the gyroscopic inertia of the rotor which is expressed by the angular momentum possessed by the rotor.

Thus

$$\text{Precession} \propto \frac{\text{Applied torque}}{\text{Angular momentum}}$$

or

$$P \propto \frac{T}{H}$$

1.10   Control of the Free Gyro to Produce a North Seeking Instrument

Clearly the free gyro does not constitute an instrument which may be called a compass. The direction of the spin axis relative to the earth's surface continually changes unless directed towards one of

the celestial poles. Even then unwanted frictional forces in the
bearings would cause the axis to wander. In order to make the spin
axis of a gyro point in any constant direction with respect to
the earth's surface, the ever present drifting and tilting caused by the
rotation of the earth, must be compensated for by causing equal and
opposite motions. To produce a compass we must produce an
instrument which will seek and settle in the meridian, and if
disturbed from the meridian will return to it.

The first step in converting a free gyro compass is to 'control' the
gyro or make it north seeking. In general this is done by creating
torque about the horizontal east west axis, which is effective when
the gyro tilts out of the horizontal. This torque will produce a
precession in azimuth which causes the spin axis to seek the
meridian.

Figure 1.19 shows a gyro rotor contained within a rotor case. The
rotor is supported through the spin axis bearings. A weight is placed

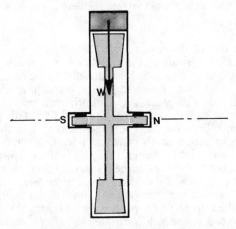

FIG. 1.19   Control weight attached to the top of the rotor case. Spin axis horizontal.

on top of the rotor casing such that when the spin axis is horizontal
the vertical through the centre of gravity of the weight passes
through the centre of the rotor. In this condition the weight will
produce no torque on the rotor and is completely ineffective.

The spin axis of the rotor, if initially horizontal, will not remain so.
The rotation of the earth will cause the spin axis to develop a tilt. If
the spin axis is directed to the east of the meridian, that end will tilt
upwards. This condition is shown in figure 1.20.

The vertical through the centre of gravity of the control weight no
longer passes through the centre of the rotor. The weight now causes
a torque about the horizontal axis which tends to topple the gyro

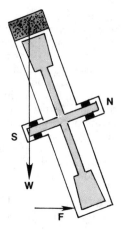

FIG. 1.20   Control weight attached to the top of the rotor case. Spin axis tilted north end upwards.

even further out of the horizontal. This effect is. as if a force was applied to the south side of the rotor casing at the bottom. If this point is imagined to be carried 90° around in the direction of spin, which is anticlockwise as viewed from the south, it will be evident that the spin axis will precess in azimuth such that the north end moves to the west, that is towards the meridian. This precession is called the control precession. The direction of spin of the rotor must be in such a direction as to produce a westerly precession of the north end of the spin axis when that end is tilted upwards, and an easterly precession of that end when it is tilted downwards.

It must be understood that the control precession will not always be directed towards the meridian. As long as the north end of the spin axis is tilted upwards the precession will carry that end towards the west. The precession will continue even after the axis has passed to the west of the meridian, and will then be carrying the north end away from the meridian. Similarly when the north end is tilted downwards and directed to the east of the meridian there will be an easterly precession taking that end away from the meridian. The effect of the control precession is discussed fully in section 1.11.

This mode of control is termed 'top heavy control', for reasons which should be obvious from inspection of figure 1.20. The same effect may be achieved by a 'bottom heavy' mode of control. Figure 1.21 illustrates a gyro rotor casing with the control weight attached to the bottom of the casing.

Again with the spin axis horizontal the weight acts vertically through the centre of the rotor and no moment about any of the three axes is produced. When the spin axis tilts out of the horizontal

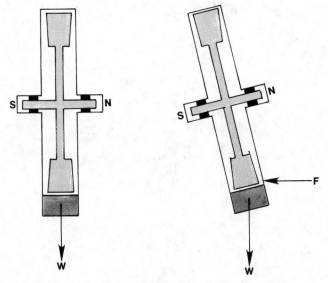

Fɪɢ. 1.21   Control weight attached to the bottom of rotor case.

as shown in figure 1.21, the vertical line of action of the weight moves away from the centre of the rotor and a torque is produced about the horizontal axis, this time acting as if to restore the spin axis to the horizontal. This therefore is a bottom heavy effect. The result of the torque about the horizontal axis is to produce a precession about the vertical axis, that is a precession in azimuth. As in the case of the top heavy control, the north end of the spin axis is required to precess to the west when that end is tilted upwards, and to the east when it is tilted downwards. The direction of spin of the bottom heavy gyro must therefore be opposite to that of the top heavy gyro. It must be clockwise as viewed from the south. (The point of application of the force F in figure 1.21 is then carried around to the north side of the western extremity of the rotor case.)

1.11   To Show that the Control Precession is Proportional to the Tilt

Figure 1.22 shows a top heavy controlled gyro with the north end of the spin axis tilted upwards by $\beta°$ (positive tilt). The control weight exerts a moment about the horizontal axis equal to Wx.
    And

$$\text{precession} = \frac{\text{applied torque}}{\text{angular momentum}}$$

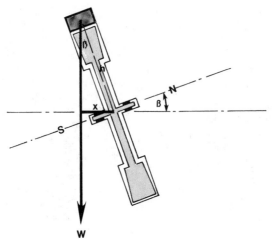

Fig. 1.22

thus

$$\text{precession} = \frac{Wx}{H}$$

and

$$x = h \sin \beta$$

thus

$$\text{precession} = \frac{Wh \sin \beta}{H}$$

Let the constants W and h be expressed by the one constant B. Then

$$\text{precession} = -\frac{B \sin \beta}{H}$$

The negative sign is necessary to comply with the convention that a precession upwards or eastwards is positive, and a precession downwards or westwards is negative.

If the tilt β is small, as is the case with a gyro compass, then

$$\text{precession} = -\frac{B\beta}{H}$$

where β is the tilt in radians.

Therefore as both B and *H* are constants determined by the construction of the gyro, it may be said that the precession is directly proportional to the tilt β.

1.12   The Effect of the Control Precession on the Free Gyro

In summary we may say that with either a top heavy or a bottom heavy gyro, the provision of a control weight causes the spin axis to precess north end to the westwards when that end is tilted above the horizontal, and north end to the eastwards when that end is tilted below the horizontal. The gyro is no longer a free gyro but is controlled. In order to look at the effect of the control precession consider a controlled gyro with the spin axis horizontal and with one end pointing to the east of north. This end will be referred to as the north end. The following account is illustrated in figure 1.23, which

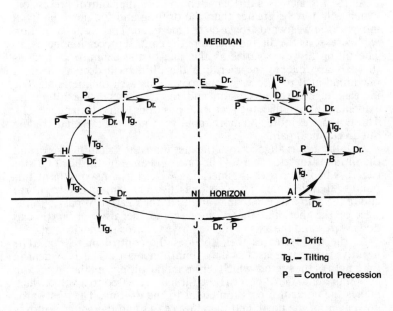

FIG. 1.23   The controlled ellipse for a north seeking gyro in north latitude.

traces the path of the projection of the north end of the spin axis onto the northern horizon. We have seen that the projection of the north end of the axis of a free gyro will be a circle around the pole, in the manner of a star. Figure 1.23 shows the elliptical path traced out by the controlled gyro commencing at A. The figure is drawn for an intermediate north latitude.

The horizontal spin axis is initially pointing to the horizon at A.

The control weight has no effect, but due to the rotation of the earth, the north end of the spin axis will immediately tilt upwards, as it is directed to the east of the meridian. It will also drift to the east as it is directed below the celestial pole. This far the gyro behaves as a free gyro, but as soon as the axis leaves the horizontal the control weight causes a precession north end westwards. It has been shown that the control precession is proportional to the tilt so that with a small tilt the control precession will be less than the drifting. The north end therefore drifts to the east but at a reduced rate. As the tilt increases then so does the control precession. There will be a value of tilt when the control precession is equal to the drifting. At this point the north end of the spin axis will cease to go to the east and will move vertically upwards under the influence of the tilting. This has occurred at point B in figure 1.23.

As the tilt increases further then so does the control precession, which will now be greater than the drifting and the north end will move to the westwards towards the meridian. This westerly motion will increase as the tilt and therefore the control precession increases. The tilting however varies as the sine of the azimuth so that as the axis approaches the meridian the tilting will decrease from a maximum at B to zero when the axis aligns with the meridian. The increase in control precession and the decrease in the tilting are evident in the length of the vectors at positions C and D in figure 1.23. The axis moves more and more rapidly towards the meridian tracing out an elliptical path.

At E the axis is aligned with the meridian, the azimuth is zero, and the tilting is therefore zero. (The rate of change of altitude of a star is zero when it crosses the meridian.) The tilt is maximum at this point so that the control precession is also a maximum and the north end of the spin axis is moving rapidly to the west. As it passes to the west of the meridian the tilting becomes negative or north end downwards and the axis begins to move towards the horizontal.

As the tilt decreases then so does the control precession. The negative tilting increases as the aximuth increases. This is evident in the length of the vectors which represent the tilting and the precession at points F and G. At point H the tilt has decreased to a value which makes the control precession equal to the drifting. The westwards movement of the north end therefore ceases and thereafter it moves to the east. The azimuth is maximum at point H so that the tilting will be maximum negative. At point I the axis is again in the horizontal and the control precession has gone to zero. As the north end of the spin axis tilts below the horizontal the control precession becomes north end eastwards and is then aiding the drifting and the axis moves rapidly towards the meridian. It is in the meridian at J and the tilting is zero. It will then become positive or north end upwards and the axis will return to the initial position with the north end directed towards the point A to complete the ellipse. The controlled gyro will oscillate in this way with the spin axis always seeking the meridian but never settling in the meridian. The ellipse traced out will be of the same dimension on each oscillation.

1.13   The Effect of Latitude on the Controlled Ellipse

A controlled gyro at the equator set initially horizontal and pointing to the east of the meridian will be subject only to tilting. The value of the rate of drifting at the equator is zero when the tilt is negligible. That end of the spin axis will therefore tilt upwards moving perpendicularly to the horizon. Immediately the axis moves out of the horizontal the control precession will carry the north end westwards towards the meridian. The maximum azimuth occurs therefore with the spin axis in the horizontal.

In the absence of any drifting the spin axis must move westwards when the north end is tilted upwards and eastwards when it is tilted down. The controlled ellipse traced out will therefore be symmetrical about the horizon as well as about the meridian. Such an ellipse is shown in figure 1.24.

In general the greater the latitude then the greater the drifting, and the greater must be the tilt to give a control precession to equal the drifting. The controlled ellipse is therefore lifted relative to the horizon by an increase of northerly latitude.

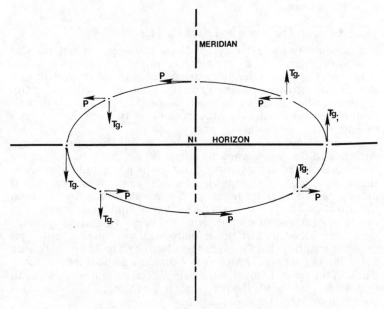

Fig. 1.24   The controlled ellipse. Gyro on equator.

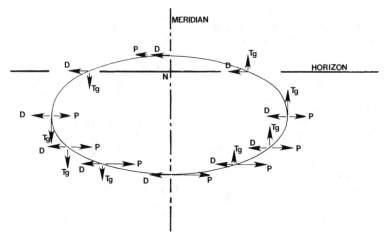

F IG. 1.25   The controlled ellipse. Gyro in south latitude.

An increase of southerly latitude will depress the controlled ellipse traced out by the north end of the spin axis, below the horizon as in south latitude the drifting of the north end will be to the west. Such an ellipse is shown in figure 1.25.

1.14   Control of the Gyro by Liquid Ballistic

The control of a gyro by solid control weight is not used in practical compasses as its use presents problems when the compass is subjected to the accelerations associated with the movement of a ship in a seaway (see Rolling Errors). Commonly used is a gravity control by a liquid ballistic, which flows between the north and south sides of the rotor under the influence of gravity when the gyro axis tilts out of the horizontal.

Consider figure 1.26(a). This shows a rotor and rotor casing. Attached to the rotor casing by a connection at the bottom of the casing is a pair of bottles or pots, one to the north and the other to the south of the east–west horizontal axis. The pipes are connected at their bases by an unrestricted pipe which allows free flow between the two pots. The pots contain a quantity of liquid; commonly used is mercury because of its high density. The pots are also connected by a pipe between their upper ends to allow equalisation of air pressure, ensuring that flow is not restricted by a build up of pressure in the top of the pots. The whole is symmetrical about the east–west axis and the centre of mass of the ballistic system must coincide with that of the rotor when the rotor axis is horizontal and the liquid is equally distributed between the pots.

In figure 1.26(a) the rotor axis is shown horizontal. The liquid will find its own horizontal and will be evenly distributed about the east–west horizontal axis. It will therefore have no effect on the gyro. That is its weight is acting vertically down through the centre of the rotor and no torque is exerted about any of the gyro axes.

In figure 1.26(b) the north end of the rotor spin axis has tilted

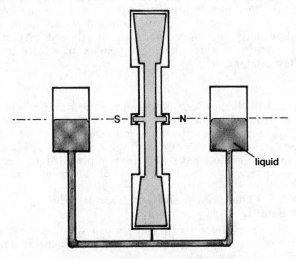

FIG. 1.26(a)   A liquid gravity control system.

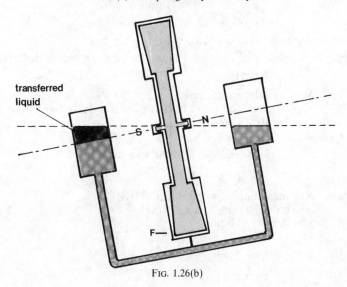

FIG. 1.26(b)

upwards, and there has been a flow of liquid to the south control pot. The imbalance now causes a torque about the horizontal east–west axis which is transmitted to the rotor via the link to the rotor casing and via the spin axis bearings. The effect is as if a force were exerted on the rotor at the bottom on the south side (at F). Note that this is identical to the action of the top mounted control weight. This arrangement therefore constitutes a top heavy gyro. The spin must be anticlockwise viewed from the south in order to create the required westerly precession when the north end tilts up. This method is used in a wide range of compasses manufactured by the Sperry Gyroscope Company Ltd.

Note

A liquid ballistic has been used in a bottom heavy configuration by S. G. Brown Ltd. in compasses which are now obsolete. To achieve bottom heaviness the liquid must be raised to the high side when the gyro axis tilts. (The Brown Type A and B compasses, which employed this method have now been superseded by the Arma Brown compass and no more will be said about this method.)

1.15   Factors Influencing the Rate of Precession with a Liquid Ballistic

As with the solid control weight we can show that the rate of precession will be proportional to the tilt, for small angles of tilt. The rate of precession is given by:

$$\text{Precession} = \frac{\text{Torque applied}}{\text{Angular momentum}} \quad \text{(section 1.9)}$$

From figure 1.27 the torque applied is given by:

Applied torque = weight of liquid transferred × distance transferred

$$= \text{W2L}$$

where   W = weight transferred
L = distance of centre of gravity of transferred weight from centre of rotor.

And

$$\text{Weight} = \text{Volume} \times \text{Density}$$

$$= a\rho h$$

where   h = mean depth of liquid transferred
a = cross sectional area of pots
ρ = density of liquid

and

$$h = L \text{ sine } \beta°$$

where $\beta°$ = tilt

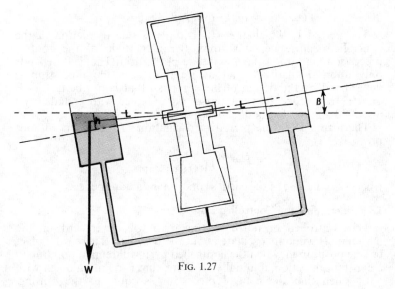

Fig. 1.27

thus

$$\text{torque applied} = a\rho L \sin\beta 2L$$
$$= 2aL^2\rho \sin\beta.$$

Let the constants $2aL^2\rho$, which are constants determined by the construction of the gyro be expressed by the constant B, then

$$\text{torque applied} = B\beta$$

(for small angles of tilt where sine β is equal to β in radians).

Note that this is the same result as that obtained for a solid weight control but in that case B was given by Wh.

Thus again

$$\text{precession} = -\frac{B\beta}{H}$$

In summary the precession depends upon:

B which is determined by the factors, cross sectional area of the pots, the distance of the centre of gravity of the pots from the centre of the rotor, and the density of the liquid;

and

H which is determined by the rate of spin of the rotor and its cross sectional moments of inertia (section 1.2):

Tilt $\cdot \beta$.

Of these the only variable is the tilt β, so that for small angles the precession is proportional to the tilt.

The Period of Oscillation of the Controlled Ellipse

The period in which the axis completes one oscillation in the controlled ellipse depends upon the magnitude of the control precession, and upon the magnitude of the drift. The drift depends only upon the latitude, but as we have seen the precession is determined by the design of the compass, that is by the factors B and *H*. In practice gyro compasses are designed with periods from about 80 minutes to about 120 minutes.

The formula for the period of oscillation (*T*), is given without proof as:

$$T = 2\pi\sqrt{\frac{H}{B\,\Omega\,\text{Cos Lat}}}$$

where Ω is the rate of the earth's rotation in radians per sec.

1.16   Damping the Controlled Ellipse

The controlled or north seeking gyro will never settle in the meridian. It will only oscillate about the meridian. There will in fact be one position in which the controlled gyro will remain pointing in a constant direction, if initially set there, that is pointing north with a tilt such that the control precession is equal to the drifting. Precession thus cancels the drifting and there is no tilting in the meridian. This will require a tilt of the north end upwards in north latitude and downwards in south latitude. The tilt necessary will increase with increasing latitude. This position however is an unstable position and any slight deviation from it will result in the axis commencing an elliptical oscillation. It will not return to the equilibrium position.

The requirement for a gyro compass is that it will initially seek and attain the meridian, and settle in an equilibrium position pointing north, and if disturbed from this position will return to it. That is the equilibrium position must be stable. The term 'damping' means the provision of a precession which will cause successive oscillations of the controlled ellipse from side to side of the meridian, to reduce in amplitude until they are infinitely small, and an equilibrium position is reached. The controlled ellipse becomes in fact a spiral inwards towards this equilibrium position, as shown in figure 1.29.

Damping may be achieved by the provision of a precession in tilt (towards the horizon), or a precession in azimuth (towards the meridian).

1.17   Damping in Tilt

To create a precession in tilt, that is about the horizontal east–west axis, a torque about the vertical axis is required (section 1.8). A number of different methods of achieving this have been, and are in use. Perhaps the method best suited to explanation of basic principles is that used in the Sperry Mark 20 gyro compass.

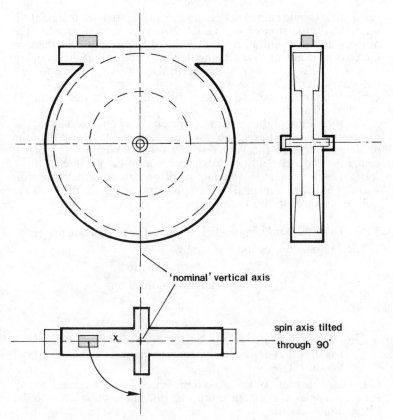

'nominal' vertical axis

spin axis tilted
through 90°

FIG. 1.28   The damping weight on top of the rotor case offset to the west of the
vertical axis. A tilt of the 'vertical' axis out of the true vertical will produce a torque
about the vertical axis equal to Wx sine tilt.

In figure 1.28 a rotor and rotor case is shown. The rotor case
carries a small weight on top and in the plane of the rotor, but offset
slightly from the vertical axis. The rotor casing is supported inside a
vertical ring, which surrounds the rotor casing in the east–west
plane. This vertical ring itself tilts about horizontal east–west
bearings, when the rotor tilts, because the rotor is supported within
the vertical ring by bearings in the vertical axis. When the rotor tilts
the vertical axis must therefore tilt also. This method of damping
requires this 'nominal' vertical axis to tilt out of the vertical.

With the spin axis horizontal the damping weight has no effect,
but when the spin axis tilts out of the horizontal, the damping weight
will exert a torque about the vertical axis which has tilted out of the

vertical. (It should help to understand why this is so if the imagination takes the tilt to extremes and visualises the vertical axis tilted to the horizontal and pointing north–south. The spin axis will then be directed vertically upwards. It should then be clear that the damping weight to the west of the nominal vertical axis will be tending to turn the vertical axis until the weight is at its lowest point.) A further explanation of this method of damping is given in the description of the Mark 20 Sperry compass.

The torque about the vertical axis results in a precession about the horizontal east–west axis, that is a precession in tilt. The offset of the damping weight to the WEST of the vertical axis in a top heavy compass produces a downwards precession of the north end of the spin axis when this end is tilted upwards, and an upwards precession when it is tilted down. The damping precession is thus always directed towards the horizon.

1.18   To Show that Damping Precession is Proportional to the Tilt

The damping precession is given by

$$\text{precession} = \frac{\text{torque applied}}{\text{angular momentum}}$$

$$= \frac{W x \sin \beta}{H}$$

where W is the damping weight
   x is the offset of the weight from the vertical axis
   β is the tilt.

Let the constants W and x be represented by the constant S, and for small angles of tilt assume that the sine of the tilt is equal to the tilt in radians. Then:

$$\text{precession} = -\frac{S \sin \beta}{H}$$

$$= -\frac{S\beta}{H}$$

where β is in radians.

As S and H are constants determined by the construction of the gyro then we may say that for small angles of tilt the precession is proportional to the tilt.

1.19   The Effect of the Damping Precession on the Controlled Ellipse

Other methods of producing the damping precession will be described with reference to particular models of gyro compass. The effect of introducing a damping precession is now considered.

Figure 1.29 shows the path traced out by the projection of the

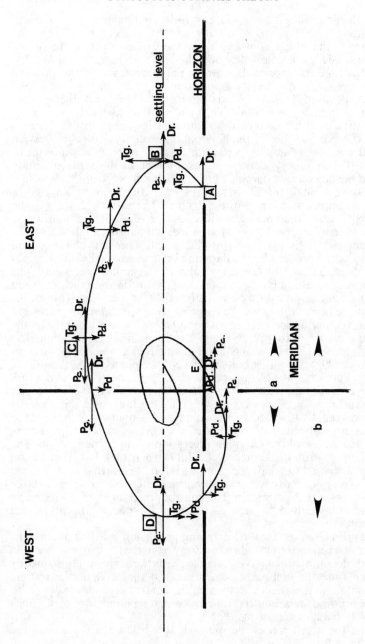

FIG. 1.29   The damped spiral for a compass damped in tilt.

north end of the spin axis of a controlled and damped gyro in north latitude. The spin axis is initially set with one end pointing at the point A, that is horizontal and directed to the east of the meridian. The following account describes how the drifting, the tilting, the control precession and the damping precession interact to produce this spiral towards the settling position.

At position A when the axis is horizontal there is neither control nor damping precessions. This end will immediately acquire a positive tilt due to the earth's rotation. It will also drift to the east. As the axis goes out of the horizontal a westerly control precession and a smaller damping precession towards the horizon are introduced. The westerly control precession reduces the easterly drifting and the downwards damping precession reduces the upwards tilting.

At position B the tilt has increased to the value which gives a control precession equal to the drifting. The easterly drifting of the north end of the spin axis will therefore cease at this point. The movement will be vertically upwards under the influence of the tilting, which is maximum at this point. The rate of tilting will however be reduced by the damping precession. As the tilt increases so does the control precession and the damping precession. The control precession is now greater than the drifting and the north end of the spin axis moves westwards towards the meridian. This means that the rate of tilting will be reducing while the damping precession is increasing. There will come a point before the spin axis reaches the meridian, when the tilting is equal to the damping precession. The tilt will therefore be a maximum at this point, which is point C in figure 1.29, and will be reducing when the spin axis aligns with the meridian, when the tilting goes to zero. As the north end of the spin axis moves to the west of the meridian the tilting of that end becomes downwards, and is now acting with the damping precession. The axis moves rapidly towards the horizontal. The amplitude of the swing in azimuth will be reduced compared with that of the controlled gyro, by the action of the damping precession towards the horizon. The maximum azimuth is reached at point D where the control precession is again equal to the drifting and therefore the north end of the spin axis ceases to move westwards and thereafter will move back to the east, towards the meridian. The control precession and the damping precession reduce to zero as the axis approaches the horizontal again.

It will be noted that the damping precession is acting against the tilting when the latter is directed away from the horizon and is acting with the tilting when it is directed towards the horizon. Consequently each time the spin axis comes back to the level of the settling position, that is the level at which the control precession is equal to the drifting, the azimuth must reduce. After a number of oscillations it will therefore reduce to zero.

As the north end of the spin axis tilts below the horizontal, the control precession becomes eastwards, that is in the same direction as the drifting. The damping precession becomes upwards. Maximum downwards tilt of the north end will occur before the axis comes into line with the meridian, where the damping precession is equal and opposite to the tilting. As it crosses the meridian the spin axis is already moving towards the horizontal. One complete oscillation about the meridian is completed when the axis arrives at position E.

The degree of damping is expressed by the 'damping factor'. This is defined as the ratio of the total swing in azimuth on two successive half cycles. In figure 1.29 the damping factor will be given by the ratio a : b.

1.20 The Settling Position

The spin axis will reach an equilibrium position at which the drifting is equalled and opposed by the control precession and the tilting is equalled and opposed by the damping precession.

For a gyro in any latitude other than the equator there will always be some amount of drifting given by 15′ sine latitude per minute of time. In north latitude the drifting will be north end to the east. There must be therefore a control precession north end to the west to oppose and counteract this. This requires an upwards tilt of the north end of the spin axis. However this tilt will also produce some amount of damping precession in a sense north end of the spin axis downwards, and this must be counteracted by an upwards tilting which is only obtained by the north end being off the meridian to the east. Thus in north latitude the compass will settle with the north end of the spin axis tilted above the horizontal and displaced to the east of the meridian. The tilt will be small and of little consequence in the operation of the compass. The displacement from the meridian

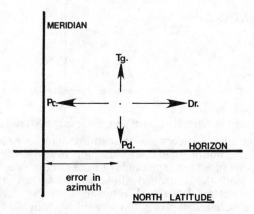

Fig. 1.30   The settling position for a compass damped in tilt. North Latitude.

constitutes an error of the compass. This error is called the latitude error. (It is also referred to as the damping error or the settling error.) The equilibrium between drifting and control precession and the tilting and the damping precession is illustrated in figure 1.30.

At the equator the drifting is zero when the spin axis is horizontal, and no compensating control precession is required. This means that the spin axis will settle in the horizontal and the damping precession will also be zero. The axis must therefore settle in the meridian where the value of the tilting is zero. In south latitude the drifting of the north end of the spin axis is to the west, requiring an easterly control precession to compensate. Consequently the north end must settle with a downwards tilt and to the west of the meridian so that the downwards tilting opposes the upwards damping precession. The sign of the latitude error therefore depends on the sign of the latitude, an easterly error being produced in north latitude and a westerly error in south latitude. A numerical analysis of the error is given in section 1.24.

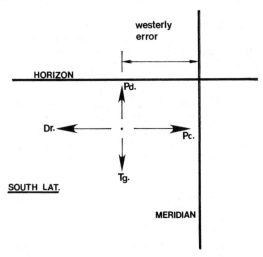

Fig. 1.31   The settling position for a compass damped in tilt. South Latitude.

1.21   Damping in Azimuth (Damping towards the Meridian)

The amplitude of successive oscillations may be reduced by a precession in azimuth, that is a precession towards the meridian. Such a precession is therefore similar to the control precession, but in order to damp the controlled ellipse it must act with the control precession, when the latter is directed towards the meridian, and must oppose the control precession when it is acting away from the meridian. Thus the motion of the axis towards the meridian will be increased and its motion away will be decreased. A damping precession in azimuth must be created in a similar way to the control precession, that is by a torque about the horizontal east–west axis. A precession merely created by the effect of gravity when the spin axis tilts however will not be suitable as its direction would only depend on whether the north end of the spin axis was tilted up or down, and could be directed towards or away from the meridian. Such a precession would only modify the rate of the control precession and would not achieve damping. It should be evident that the damping precession must always be directed towards the meridian.

This may be achieved by creating the precession in azimuth by a torque about the horizontal axis by a flow of liquid under the influence of gravity when the axis tilts, but causing a lag between cause and effect by introducing a restriction to the flow. The action of the ballistic will then be out of phase with the tilt which caused the flow. Figure 1.32(a) shows the direction of the precession in azimuth

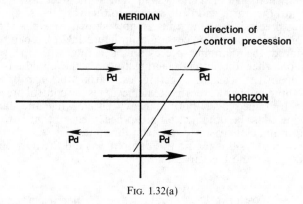

Fig. 1.32(a)

without any restriction causing delayed action. The direction of rotation of the rotor is clockwise viewed from the south, i.e. that direction appropriate to a bottom heavy compass. The control precession is produced by a bottom heavy effect while the damping precession is produced by a top heavy effect. The resulting precessions will therefore be of opposite direction.

Figure 1.32(b) now shows the effect of introducing a lag in the action of the damping precession equal to one quarter of the period of oscillation.

It will be noted now that the direction of the precession is now always towards the meridian. What has occurred is that the precession which originally was caused when the axis was in the north end up and to the east quadrant, now does not occur until the north end is up and to the west. The direction which originally

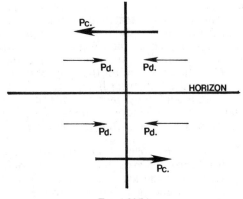

FIG. 1.32(b)

occurred when the north end was up and to the west now does not occur until the north end is down and to the west and so on. If the damping precession acting thus is now shown together with the direction of the control precession as in figure 1.32(c), it can be seen that indeed the damping precession is acting with the control precession when the latter is acting towards the meridian and is acting against it when it is acting away from the meridian. It is important to note however that to achieve this the control precession must be obtained by a bottom heavy effect, while the damping precession must be obtained by a top heavy effect, that is with the rotor rotating clockwise viewed from the south. The Anschutz gyro compass employs this method of damping, as did the now obsolete Brown types A and B compasses.

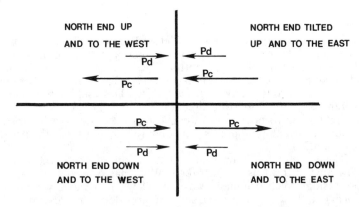

FIG. 1.32(c)

It is important to realise that the damping precession produced by this method can only be produced when there is a change of tilt of the spin axis. No damping precession can be caused when the spin axis has a constant tilt. This is because the delaying action of the restriction to the flow of the liquid, can only be effective when there is, in fact, a flow. A constant tilt of the axis will not cause any transfer of liquid so that the delaying action is ineffective. Under these circumstances the damping torque will always act in the opposite direction to the control torque thus merely reducing its effect. The importance of this is that when the axis has settled it will have a constant tilt, and therefore in the settling position there will be no damping precession. The significance of this may now be evident to the student. It will however be discussed further when the settling position is discussed in section 1.23.

1.22   Path Traced Out by the Spin Axis of the Gyro Damped in Azimuth

Figure 1.33 shows a damped spiral traced out by the north end of the spin axis of a gyrocompass damped in azimuth. The direction of the vectors representing the damping precession assume that the delay in the action of the damping torque is exactly a quarter of the cycle. This is not necessarily so and the exact shape of the trace may vary. It is important to note however that the axis will cross the meridian moving horizontally, because at the moment of being in the meridian the tilting is zero, and there is no precession in tilt. On the other hand the axis will reach maximum azimuth and commence moving back towards the meridian before it reaches the settling level, and under the action of the damping precession towards the meridian will move in azimuth more rapidly when moving towards the

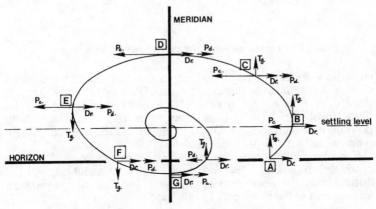

Fig. 1.33   The damped spiral for a compass damped in azimuth.

C

meridian than when moving away from the meridian. It is when the axis is moving towards the meridian that the upwards or downwards tilt is increasing so that the axis will reach the meridian with a reduced tilt on successive oscillations, and must eventually settle.

1.23   The Settling Position for a Compass Damped in Azimuth

When the compass is settled the spin axis has a constant tilt. The delaying action of the damping arrangement will therefore have no effect as there is no flow of liquid (see section 1.21). The damping element is then acting merely as an additional control element, but as the damping torque is produced by a top heavy effect whereas the control precession is produced by a bottom heavy effect, the damping precession will just reduce the effect of the control precession. The

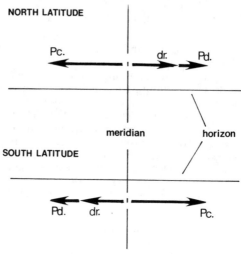

FIG. 1.34   The settling position for a compass damped in azimuth.

compass will settle with a tilt of its spin axis such that the combined effect of the control and damping torques, (Pc − Pd), exactly balances the drifting. There is no precession in the vertical plane so that the tilting must also be zero to produce an equilibrium. The settling position must be therefore with the spin axis in the meridian. There is no latitude error.

For a compass in north latitude the drifting will be clockwise, or north end to the east. The precession which equals and opposes the drifting must be north end to the west and this will require an upwards tilt of the north end. In this condition:

$$- Pc + Pd + Dg = 0.$$

In south latitude the drifting will be anticlockwise or north end to the west. A downwards tilt of the north end is therefore required to give a control precession of opposite direction. In this condition:

$$+ Pc - Pd - Dg = 0.$$

A compass damped in azimuth therefore will settle with the spin axis aligned with the meridian but with a small upwards tilt of the north end in the northern hemisphere, and a small downwards tilt of that end in the southern hemisphere. Such a compass is not subject to the latitude error (in contrast to the compass damped in tilt). Figure 1.34 illustrates the settling position for a compass damped in azimuth.

OPERATIONAL ERRORS OF THE GYRO

There are two errors of the marine gyro compass, for which compensation must be made in the use of the gyro. In addition there are errors which must by their nature, be eliminated as far as possible in the design of the compass, but which remain as small residual uncorrectable errors, of which the operator should be aware.

1.24   Latitude Error (Damping Error)

It has been shown that a gyro compass which is damped in tilt will settle with a displacement from the meridian (see section 1.21). It has also been shown that compasses damped in azimuth are NOT subject to this error (see section 1.23). The magnitude of the error will be determined by the design and construction of the individual compass, and it may be assessed for any particular design by considering the equilibrium condition at the settling position for a compass damped in tilt.

At the settling position there must be an equilibrium between:

1. Drifting, (Ω sine latitude per minute).   (section 1.5)

2. Tilting, (Ω cosine latitude · sine azimuth per minute).
                                                                (section 1.5)

3. Control precession, $\left(-\dfrac{B\beta}{H} \right)$.   (section 1.15)

4. Damping precession, $\left(-\dfrac{S\beta}{H} \right)$.   (section 1.18).

Thus,

$$\text{control precession} = \text{drifting} \tag{1}$$

and

$$\text{damping precession} = \text{tilting} \tag{2}$$

From (1)

$$-\frac{B\beta}{H} + \Omega \text{ sine latitude} = 0.$$

From (2)

$$-\frac{S\beta}{H} + \Omega \text{ cosine latitude sine azimuth} = 0.$$

The constants B, S, and H are determined by the construction of the compass, and may be quantified for any particular design. Thus from equation (1) the tilt at the settling position can be found for any latitude. Using this tilt in equation (2) the azimuth at the settling position can be found. This azimuth will be the latitude error for the latitude assumed in the equations.

Thus from (1)

$$-\beta = \frac{\Omega H \text{ sine lat.}}{B}$$

and in (2)

$$\text{sine azimuth} = \frac{S \text{ sine lat.}}{B \text{ cosine lat.}}$$

As the error will be small sine azimuth $\simeq$ azimuth in radians

$$\text{Az}^c = \frac{S}{B} \tan \text{ lat.}$$

$$\text{Az}^\circ = \frac{S}{B} 57 \cdot 3 \tan \text{ lat.}$$

A graph of latitude error against latitude will appear as in figure 1.35.

The damping error is therefore shown to be proportional to the tangent of the latitude. It should be noted that the tangent approaches infinity as the latitude approaches 90°. The error may be very large in high latitudes. Typical values may be about 1·5° in latitude 45°, and 2·5° in latitude 60°. On the same compass the error would be over 5° in latitude 75°.

1.25   Course Latitude and Speed Error (Steaming Error)

The compass will settle with respect to a false meridian if the vessel is moving across the surface of the earth with a velocity which has a northerly or a southerly component. Such a velocity will produce a false tilting of the spin axis. Only if the course is east or west will there be no such false tilting. Consider a vessel which is steaming north at 20 knots. A star which is on the observer's meridian to the north will appear to rise in the sky by 20 minutes of arc per hour. This constitutes a false rising of the star, which to a stationary observer would be at maximum altitude and therefore not changing

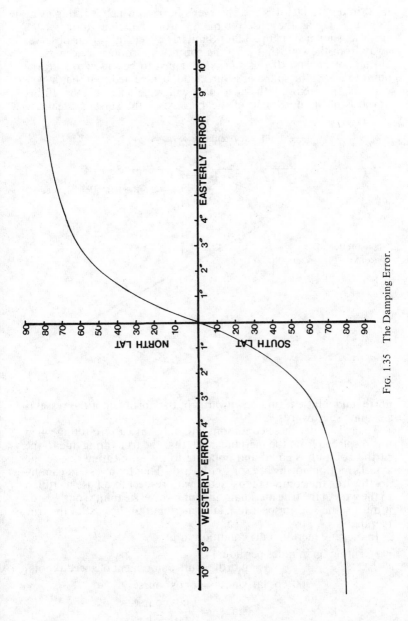

Fig. 1.35 The Damping Error.

its altitude. (In fact it is the observer's horizon which is tilting away from the star as the observer moves around the curvature of the earth as shown in figure 1.36.) Similarly a velocity of an observer away from the star, that is to the south will produce a decrease of altitude of the star. If this star is imagined to be the gyro star, the point to which the spin axis is directed it can be deduced that a gyro with its spin axis in the meridian will experience a false tilting upwards of the north end of the spin axis if the vessel is steaming

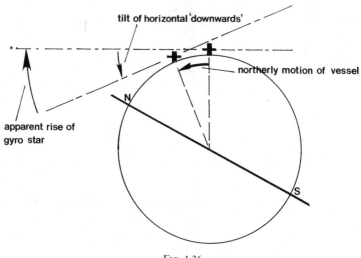

FIG. 1.36

north, and a false tilting downwards of the north end if the vessel is steaming southwards.

The axis under these conditions will only have a zero tilting when it is displaced from the meridian such that the true tilting due to the earth's rotation is equal and opposite to the false tilting due to the vessel's motion northwards or southwards. Thus for a vessel steaming northwards the compass must settle with respect to a false meridian to the west of the true meridian, and for a vessel steaming southwards it must settle with respect to a false meridian to the east of the true meridian.

In the false meridian the conditions are:

Tilting (in minutes per hour)
$$= \text{North–south component of speed (knots)}$$
$$900' \cos \text{lat. } \sin Az = v \cos \text{course}$$
$$\sin Az = \frac{v \cos \text{course}}{900 \cos \text{lat.}}$$

As the error is small sin Az is equal to the Az in radians, and this will be the error of the gyro.

Thus

$$\text{error}^c = \frac{v \cos \text{course}}{900 \cos \text{lat.}}$$

$$\text{error}^\circ = \frac{v \cos \text{course} \cdot 180}{900 \cos \text{lat.} \, \pi}$$

$$= \frac{v \cos \text{course}}{5\pi \cos \text{lat.}}$$

It should be clear from this formula that the magnitude of the steaming error does not depend in any way upon the compass itself, its design or characteristics. The error is the same for all compasses, being determined by the course, speed and latitude of the vessel.

This is an approximate formula which is adequate for all practical purposes at sea in normal navigable latitudes. The error varies as the secant of the latitude so that as the latitude approaches 90° the error approaches infinity. Large errors will be obtained in high latitudes. A speed of 20 knots on a northerly course in latitude 60° gives an error of $2\frac{1}{2}°$. The same conditions in latitude 75° give an error of 5°.

The approximations inherent in this formula are valid only if the speed of the vessel is small compared with the linear speed of the earth's rotation. This will always be the case in a marine craft in normal navigable latitudes. At high speed such as that encountered in aircraft and in any craft in very high latitudes a more accurate formula must be used. The large errors due to the high speeds and the effect of the considerable accelerations imposed upon the compass by aircraft manoeuvres, preclude the use of the marine gyro compass in aircraft.

1.26 Accurate Formula for Course Latitude and Speed Error

If the velocity of the vessel across the earth's surface is considerable compared with the earth's rotation then the error becomes large. It can no longer be assumed that the sine or tangent of the error is equal to the error in radians. Furthermore the east–west component of the vessel's velocity will increase or decrease the effective velocity of the earth's east–west rotation. If the vessel is steaming to the west then effectively the earth's rotation is reduced. It then becomes $900' \cos \text{lat.} - v \sin \text{course}$. If the vessel is steaming eastwards then effectively the earth's rotation is increased. It then becomes $900' \cos \text{lat.} + v \sin \text{course}$ per hour. Also the motion of the vessel northwards along the false meridian will be $(v \cos \text{course}) \cos$ error.

Thus the condition when the tilting due to the earth's rotation is equal and opposite to the tilting due to the vessel's speed will be:

$$(900' \cos \text{lat.} \pm v \sin \text{co}) \sin Az = v \cos \text{co} \cos Az$$

$$\text{Tan} \, Az = \frac{v \cos \text{co}}{900 \cos \text{lat.} \pm v \sin \text{co}}$$

1.27   The Change in the Course and Speed Error

The approximate formula for the course and speed error gives, for a vessel steaming north at 20 knots in latitude 60°, an error of $2\frac{1}{2}$ W. If that vessel now alters course by 180° and steams south the error will become $2\frac{1}{2}$ E. The compass will resettle in a position 5° to the east of the original settling position. In order to resettle the axis will execute a damped spiral and will therefore for a period following the alteration be unsteady. A series of manoeuvres in rapid succession could produce serious errors in the compass. There are two ways in which this problem may be tackled.

The course latitude and speed error may be eliminated entirely by creating a precession of the spin axis which is equal and opposite to the false tilting of the axis caused by the north–south component of the vessel's speed. The tilting occurs at the rate of this component, $(v \cdot \cos \text{course})$ (section 1.25). The precession to compensate for the false tilting must therefore be equal to $v \cos \text{course}$. The compass will then settle in the true meridian, (damping error corrected), and will therefore not require to resettle after an alteration. This method is employed in the Arma Brown Compass and the Sperry Mark 20, these compasses being discussed in more detail in the chapters devoted to them.

The course latitude and speed error is, in some compasses, allowed to occur and is then apparently corrected by shifting the lubber line by an amount equal to the error. In other compasses the error must be allowed for by the navigator, who extracts the error from tables supplied. In each case the compass will require to resettle after each alteration of course or speed, and the unsteadiness associated with the damped spiral must be avoided. This is done by causing the compass to precess directly to the new settling position by making use of another, otherwise unwanted, effect of the alteration of course or speed. This is the Ballistic Deflection which is described in section 1.32. This section fully explains how the ballistic deflection is used to solve the problem of the change in the course and speed error.

1.28   The Effect of Ship Motions on the Gyroscope

The correct and accurate operation of the gyro compass depends upon the effect of gravity on the control and damping element of the compass. The acceleration due to the earth's gravity acts vertically downwards and defines the horizontal for the compass. If the compass is subjected to other accelerations such as those associated with the motion of a ship in a seaway, the compass will react to these accelerations as they will be indistinguishable from that of the earth's gravity. The compass will sense the resultant of all the accelerations to which it is subjected, and this resultant will define a 'false' vertical and thus a false horizontal. The effect of ship motions are called Rolling Errors but they are not errors in the sense that they can be assessed and allowed for, but their effect is to produce spurious wandering of the compass. They must therefore be eliminated as far as possible in the design of the compass so that the navigator has no part to play in their compensation.

1.29 The First Rolling Error

A body which is set swinging pendulously, and whose mass is distributed preferentially in one vertical plane, is subject to dynamic forces which turn the plane in which the mass lies, into the plane of the swing. The vertical ring of the rotor suspension frame of a gyro compass will be affected in this way, the plane of the ring having a tendency to turn into the plane of the swing caused by the ship movement. The maximum torque occurs when the plane of the ring is at an angle of 45° to the plane of the swing. As the vertical ring surrounds the rotor casing in the east–west plane this will occur when the compass is swinging in the intercardinal planes, that is NE/SW or NW/SE.

Because of the construction of the suspension axes of the gyro the vertical ring must be constrained in the east–west plane. If there is a torque which acts to turn the vertical ring out of this plane then there must be a reactionary torque on the member that is restraining the ring. On some compasses this is the rotor itself (when the connection between the rotor case and the vertical ring is through a horizontal east–west bearing). In this case the reactionary torque acts on the rotor and will precess the rotor in tilt. The subsequent flow of liquid in the control element will then cause a north or a south heaviness which will precess the rotor in azimuth.

This is not a serious problem as it can be entirely eliminated by attaching balancing weights to the vertical ring to equalise the distribution of the mass of the ring and compensator weights in all vertical planes. There will be one weight projecting out on the north side of the vertical ring and another on the south side. They are carefully adjusted in the factory or workshop such that the centre of gravity of the ring and weights still remains at the centre of the rotor, and that the moments of inertia of the ring is the same about the axes in the north–south and the east–west planes. The vertical ring then acts as if it were spherical and there is no tendency for any preferential vertical plane to align itself with the plane of the swing.

In some compasses the arrangement of the suspension axes is such that the vertical ring is constrained in the east–west plane, not by the rotor, but by the non-sensitive part of the compass (in the Sperry Mark 20 by the phantom element). The connection between the vertical ring and the rotor is through a vertical axis, so that no torque is put on the rotor and the problem does not exist.

1.30   Intercardinal Rolling Error

This is an error produced on the control element by the accelerations associated with the motion of a ship in a seaway. These accelerations are sensed by the gravity control element which cannot distinguish them from the acceleration due to gravity. When the compass is swinging in an arc, the centre of which does not coincide with the centre of the compass, the compass is always being accelerated towards the mean position of the swing. The acceleration will only be zero when the compass is passing through the mean position. The acceleration of the swing creates a false vertical which is the resultant between it and the acceleration due to gravity. The liquid in the control element will associate itself with the false verticals producing north or south heaviness, and the compass will associate itself with the false verticals in its gimbals.

Consider a compass swinging in a north–south plane. (This may be caused by the vessel rolling when on an east–west course or pitching when on a north–south course.) When the swing displaces the compass to the northwards, the compass is being accelerated towards the south, that is either the northwards velocity is decreasing or the southwards velocity is increasing. The acceleration of the liquid relative to the compass is therefore towards the north and a north heaviness will result. Similarly when the compass is displaced towards the south, the compass is being accelerated northwards and the liquid creates a south heaviness.

The angular displacement of the vertical from the true vertical represents a false tilt ($\Delta\beta$), and a precession in azimuth will result due to the control element responding to this tilt equal to $B\Delta\beta/H$. However this precession will change sign on opposite sides of the

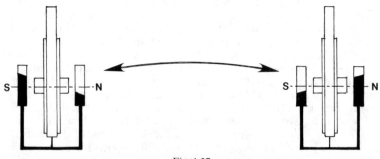

Fig. 1.37

swing as a north heaviness alternates with a south heaviness. Any error thus cancels out over the period of the swing and no error is caused by a swing in the north–south plane.

Consider now the compass swinging in the east–west plane. The false vertical will be displaced from the true vertical in the east–west plane. As there is no north–south component of the acceleration there will be no transfer of liquid, and therefore no north or south heaviness. However if the compass is swinging in an intercardinal plane then the accelerations have a north–south component and also an east–west component. The north–south component will cause an alternating north or south heaviness as described for the north–south swing, and the east–west component will cause the false vertical to swing out of the north–south plane. The action of the compass in its gimbals associating itself with the false vertical will cause a torque about the vertical axis as well as about the horizontal east–west axis, and this gives rise to a precession in tilt which, unlike the precession in azimuth, does not cancel on opposite sides of the swing.

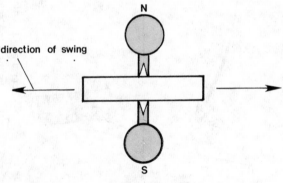

FIG. 1.38

Consider figure 1.39 which shows a gyro rotor case supported within a vertical ring which surrounds the rotor case in the east–west plane, that is in the plane of the rotor. The control element is attached to the vertical ring and the torque created by a north or south heaviness is transferred to the rotor case through the connection at the bottom of the rotor case, this connection being in the vertical axis, in its designed position. (For a more detailed description of this arrangement see the construction of the Sperry Mark 20.) Figure 1.39(a) shows the compass viewed from the south when at the south-west extremity of a south-west/north-east swing. The northerly component of the acceleration has caused a south heaviness. The easterly component of the acceleration has caused the connection at the bottom of the rotor case to go to the west of the true vertical.

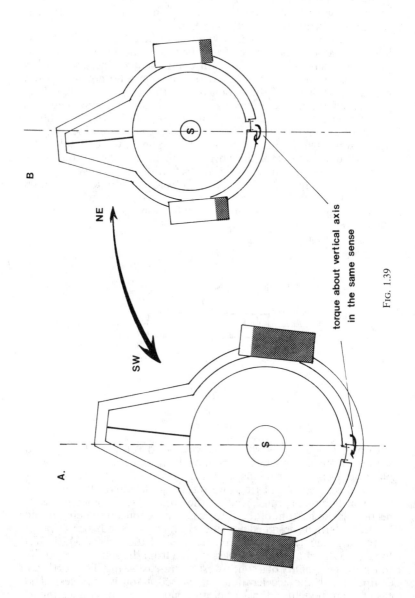

torque about vertical axis in the same sense

Fig. 1.39

Thus the south heaviness will result in a torque about the vertical which is clockwise as viewed from above and this will give a precession in tilt, north end upwards. There will also be a precession in azimuth north end to the west, but this will be cancelled by the easterly precession on the other half of the swing. When at the north-east extremity, as shown in figure 1.39(b), there is a north heaviness combined with a movement of the connection to the rotor case to the east of the true vertical. The precession in azimuth is to the east and of opposite sign to that on the other half of the swing but the precession in tilt is again north end upwards, as the torque about the vertical axis is again clockwise as viewed from above. As long as the swinging continues therefore there is a continual precession north end upwards.

The rolling precession in tilt will cause the compass to settle where it is opposed by the tilting due to the earth's rotation. For a compass damped in tilt the condition at the settling position will be:

Tilting = damping precession + rolling precession.

For a compass damped in azimuth the condition will be:

Tilting = rolling precession.

The tilting may only be found out of the meridian, and as the precession due to the rolling may be large, the error caused may also be considerable. In fact in practice, as a ship's motion tends to vary with respect to roll amplitude and acceleration the compass will not settle with a constant error but will be unsteady with large unknown errors.

1.31 Elimination of Intercardinal Rolling Error

The effect of the intercardinal rolling error as described only occurs if the control element reacts instantaneously to the accelerations imposed upon it by the vessel's motion. This will be so if a solid weight is used to achieve top or bottom heavy control. It will only be the case with a liquid control element if there is free and unrestricted flow of liquid between the north and south pots. This is not so as the pipes which interconnect the pots are of relatively small bore compared with the diameter of the pots. This restriction will produce a lag between the acceleration due to the motion and the resultant flow of liquid. It will also to some extent limit the amount of liquid transferred. If the restriction of the bore of the pipes is such that a 90° phase lag between the swing of the compass and the maximum displacement of liquid is caused, that is if the delay is equal to exactly one quarter of the period of the swing, then the maximum displacement of liquid will occur, not at the extremities of the swing, but as the compass passes through the mean position of the swing. If this is so then no rolling error occurs.

To understand why this is so it must be remembered that at the moment that the compass passes through the central position of the swing, the acceleration of the swing is zero. The compass vertical therefore coincides with the true vertical, and any north or south heaviness cannot cause a torque about the vertical as its effect is transmitted to the rotor case through a connection in the vertical axis (see figure 1.31). The alternate north and south heaviness causes only torques about the horizontal axis which cancel over the period of the swing. Any torques which occur about the vertical axis just before or after the compass passes through the mean position will now cancel as they will be of opposite sense.

The delay caused by the design of the control element must be based upon an assumed period of oscillation. As this period is in practice determined by the vessel's motion, it will in fact vary between different ship's and will vary for any particular ship, with weather conditions and with conditions of loading. If the period of oscillation of the compass coincides with the period assumed in the design of the compass then the error will be eliminated but for any other period of oscillation there will be some residual error.

If the period of the compass oscillation is greater than that assumed then the restricted bore will undercompensate and maximum head of liquid will occur before the compass passes through the mean position. In this case there will be a residual error of the same sign as if there were no restriction, that is for the example used in section 1.30, west for an oscillation in the SW/NE plane, and east for an oscillation in the NW/SE plane. This is the direction of the error associated with a top heavy compass. If the period of the compass is less than that assumed there will be an overcompensation. The

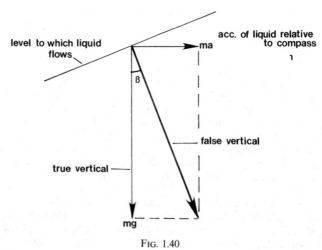

FIG. 1.40

maximum head of liquid will occur after the compass has passed through the mean position and residual error of the opposite sign will occur.

The residual errors are reduced by adopting an excessive period of oscillation in the design of the compass, so that there will always be an overcompensation under normal ship motion conditions. This is then compensated for by creating some top-heaviness by means of compensator weights attached to the top of the control pots. By careful selection of the amount of top-heaviness introduced the residual errors can be reduced to acceptable limits over the normal range of rolling periods encountered on ships. The compensator weights are adjusted in manufacture after rolling error tests and should not be disturbed. It should be realised that small residual errors may be experienced during periods of sustained rolling. Specifications for a gyro compass supplied by the manufacturer usually state the results of extensive rolling error tests after compensation has been adjusted.

1.32   Ballistic Deflection

Ballistic deflection is a precession which results from accelerations imparted to the compass by a change in the speed and/or the course of the vessel. If the vessel is steaming north and increases speed then the vessel will exert a force on the compass which will accelerate it northwards. There will be a reactionary force acting on the liquid in the control element towards the south. The liquid will therefore be accelerated to the south relative to the compass. (The compass is accelerated towards the north while the liquid, due to its inertia, tends to remain behind, and there is a flow of liquid into the south pots.) This will also occur if the vessel is steaming south and decreases her speed, or if the course is altered towards the north, thus effectively increasing the northerly component of the speed.

If the vessel is steaming south and increases speed, or is steaming north and decreases speed, or if the course is altered towards the south, all of which constitute a southerly acceleration, the liquid will be accelerated towards the north relative to the compass and a north heaviness will result.

Note that the acceleration imparted to the compass is effectively creating a false vertical and hence a false horizontal. The false vertical is the resultant of the acceleration due to gravity and that due to the vessels change of motion, as shown in figure 1.40. The control element will remain in the true horizontal due to the gyroscopic inertia, but the liquid will associate itself with the false horizontal and flow to produce the north or south heaviness.

If a north heaviness results from a southerly acceleration, a precession in azimuth will occur which is in the sense north end to the east. If a south heaviness results from a northerly acceleration, the north end of the spin axis will precess towards the west. The rate of precession will be proportional to the acceleration causing it. The precession however will continue for as long as the acceleration continues, so that for a given alteration of course and/or speed the total change in azimuth will be constant, irrespective of the rate at which the manoeuvre is carried out.

1.33   Formula for the Ballistic Deflection

Figure 1.40 illustrates the vectors representing the acceleration due to gravity, and that due to the vessel's change of motion. The tilt of the false horizontal is shown as β.

In figure 1.40 the tilt β is given by:

$$\tan \beta = \frac{ma}{mg}$$

or considering β to be small:

$$\beta = \frac{a}{g}$$

where β is expressed in radians.

The precession is therefore given by:

$$- \frac{\beta B}{H}$$

(see section 1.15).

Thus

$$\text{precession} = - \frac{Ba}{Hg} \text{ rads./sec.}$$

The total change of azimuth is found by multiplying this rate of precession by the time in seconds during which the precession continues.

Thus

$$\text{change of azimuth} = - \frac{Bat}{Hg} \text{ radians.}$$

The negative sign indicates that a northerly ($+$ve) acceleration will produce a westerly ($-$ve) change of azimuth. A southerly ($-$ve) acceleration will produce an easterly ($+$ve) change of azimuth.

1.34   Eliminating the Effects of Ballistic Deflection

The wandering of the compass during a manoeuvre, which has been described as ballistic deflection, will cause an unsteady compass after the manoeuvre while the compass resettles, tracing out the damped spiral in doing so. It is possible however to use the ballistic deflection to advantage, to solve the problem introduced in section 1.27. It was explained that an unsteady compass is produced after a manoeuvre due to the need to resettle after a change in the value of the course and speed error. Both of these unwanted effects are caused by a change in the north–south component of the vessel's speed.

The ballistic deflection is made to deflect the spin axis directly to the new settling position, thus obviating the need to execute a damped spiral to resettle.

Fortunately the ballistic deflection is always in the direction required to achieve this. Consider a vessel steaming north at 20 knots in latitude 60°, which alters course by 180° to steam south. In section 1.27 it was shown that in this case the course and speed error will change from $2\frac{1}{2}°$ W to $2\frac{1}{2}°$ E. The axis must therefore precess 5° to the east to achieve the new settling position. We have seen in section 1.32 that this same manoeuvre will produce a ballistic deflection north end to the east.

The amount of the ballistic deflection must be just sufficient for the spin axis to reach the new settling position and no more. For any particular design of compass the amount of the deflection (precession), will depend upon the design of the control element (size of the pots, their distance from the centre of the rotor, the density of the liquid), and the angular momentum of the rotor (see section 1.15). The same factors determine the period of oscillation of the spin axis in the controlled ellipse.

For ballistic deflection to be equal to the change in the course and speed error then:

$$\frac{\text{Bat}}{\text{Hg}} = \frac{v' \cos \text{Co}'}{R\Omega \cos \text{lat.}} - \frac{v \cos \text{Co}}{R\Omega \cos \text{lat.}}$$

where $v \cos \text{Co}$ and $v' \cos \text{Co}'$ are the north–south components of the vessel's speed before and after an alteration, and $R\Omega$ is the rate of the earth's rotation at the equator. If a, g and v are expressed in m/s^2 and m/s as appropriate then $R\Omega$ must be in metres per second.

The earth's linear rate of rotation at the equator is one equatorial circumference in one sidereal day (almost 24 hours).

The linear rate of rotation at the equator in metres per second is therefore given by:

$$\frac{2\pi R}{24 \times 60 \times 60} \text{ m/s}$$

or $R\Omega$ where

$$\Omega = \frac{2\pi}{24 \times 60 \times 60} \text{ rads./sec.}$$

Thus

$$\frac{\text{Bat}}{\text{Hg}} = \frac{v \cos \text{Co} - v' \cos \text{Co}'}{R\Omega \cos \text{lat.}}$$

$$\frac{\text{Bat}}{\text{Hg}} = \frac{at}{R\Omega \cos \text{lat.}}$$

$$\frac{H}{B\Omega \cos \text{lat.}} = \frac{R}{g}$$

and the period of the undamped ellipse $= T = 2\pi \sqrt{\dfrac{H}{B\Omega \cos \text{lat.}}}$

or

$$T = 2\pi \sqrt{\frac{R}{g}}$$

$$= 2\pi \sqrt{\frac{6\,378\,388}{9 \cdot 81}}$$

$$= 5066 \cdot 416 \text{ secs.}$$

$$= 84 \cdot 44 \text{ minutes.}$$

Thus if the undamped period of the compass is made to be 84·4 minutes then the ballistic deflection will be just sufficient to precess the compass to its new settling position after an alteration of course or speed. This period is called the Schuler period, and a gyro "so designed" is said to be Schuler tuned.

An inspection of the formula for the undamped period will show it to be dependent partly upon the latitude. Although it is possible to design the control element of the compass such that the period changes with an adjustment for latitude this is not done in commercial compasses and they are Schuler tuned for a standard latitude. The errors incurred in other latitudes are small enough to be tolerated.

1.35   Ballistic Deflection in Compasses which are not Schuler Tuned

In modern compasses it is often the practice to eliminate the course and speed error at source by the provision of a precession in tilt equal and opposite to the false tilting caused by the vessels north or south movement. This was explained in sections 1.26 and 1.27. If this is done however there is no necessity for the compass to resettle after an alteration of course or speed because both before and after the manoeuvre the error is zero and there is no change in the value of the error. The ballistic deflection remains therefore as an unwanted precession during the alteration, and the compass will be subsequently unsteady as it resettles. In such compasses the ballistic deflection must be kept to a minimum by reducing the effect of the control element for any given tilt. This will also increase the period of the undamped oscillation while settling. This is undesirable in that the compass will take longer to settle and of course to resettle after a disturbance from the settling position. The design is therefore a compromise and a figure of about 120 minutes for the period is usually chosen (Sperry Mark 20 and Arma Brown).

1.36 Ballistic Tilt

If a precession which is proportional to the tilt of the spin axis is used for damping (i.e. damping in tilt), then the false tilt introduced by an acceleration of the vessel, which causes ballistic deflection, will also cause a precession in tilt, by the action of the damping element. As well as deflecting in azimuth the compass will also deflect in tilt. An acceleration of the vessel to the southwards will cause a torque about the vertical axis which is clockwise from above. A precession in tilt north end upwards results. Similarly an acceleration to the northwards will produce a precession in tilt north end downwards.

In consequence of this, in compasses which use the ballistic deflection to compensate for the change in the course latitude and speed error, the axis will arrive at the new settling azimuth slightly displaced in tilt from the settling position. The compass will therefore require to execute a small damped spiral until the spin axis truly settles. This is shown in figure 1.41 in which the original westerly steaming error is changed into an easterly error by an alteration of course from northerly to southerly. The ballistic deflection resulting from such an alteration it has been shown, precesses the north end of the spin axis to the east. If the compass is Schuler tuned, it will arrive in the correct azimuth at the end of the alteration. The ballistic tilt however precesses the north end upwards so that the new compass north is reached with a displacement in tilt upwards from

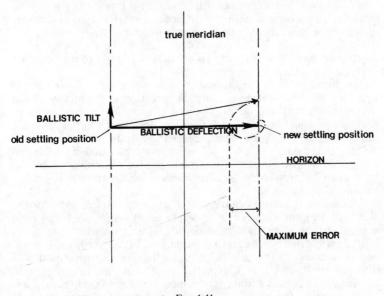

FIG. 1.41

the settling position. The damped spiral traced out by the spin axis, while settling will thus produce an error in azimuth which will reach a maximum after one quarter of the period of the oscillation, that is after about 22 minutes. Thereafter the error will reduce and on succeeding oscillations may be considered negligible.

1.37   The Directional Gyro

Accurate indication of the true meridian by a marine gyro compass is dependent upon the sensing of the east–west plane as indicated by the rotation of the earth, and the true vertical as indicated by the earth's gravitational attraction. If the compass is subjected to additional velocities and accelerations, these will also be sensed and will mask the true direction of the earth's rotation and its gravity. Velocities and accelerations experienced on a marine craft in normal navigable latitudes are small enough compared with those of the earth to render any errors which may be caused, within tolerable limits and correctable. This will not be the case however if the velocity and acceleration of the vessel becomes comparable to those of the earth and its gravitation. This may occur if the vessel's velocity increases, for example if the compass is placed aboard an aircraft, or if the linear rate of the earth's rotation decreases as it does if the compass is taken to high latitudes. In both cases errors become large and the gyro can no longer be considered as providing a north reference.

A directional reference may still be obtained however by using the gyroscope as a directional gyro. In general marine gyro compasses do not have this facility, but the Arma Brown compass, which was designed originally for purposes other than in the marine environment, is so provided. A short explanation of the use of the compass in this mode is therefore in order.

The function of a directional gyro is to provide a directional reference, which is not necessarily the direction of the meridian, but which is constant over a short period of time. The period must be regarded as short because once the gyro deviates from the reference direction there is no provision to cause the gyro to return to it, in the manner that the marine gyro will return to the meridian if it is caused to deviate from it. Instead the direction which is indicated by the gyro must be monitored by astronomical observation or by other azimuthal indications.

A directional gyro is obtained by correcting the free gyro for the effects of drift and tilting, caused by the earth's rotation. It has been explained that a free gyro placed with its axis horizontal in north latitude will drift, north end to the east, and tilt upwards if the north end is directed to the east of the meridian, or downwards if it is directed to the west of the meridian. A constant reference with respect to the earth's surface is obtained if a precession in azimuth is applied equal and opposite to the drift, and a precession in tilt equal

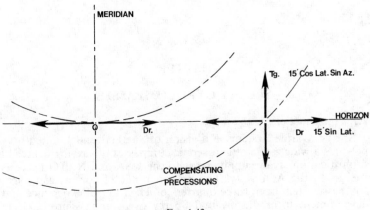

FIG. 1.42

and opposite to the tilting. These precessions must be constant for any given latitude and for any given direction indicated by the spin axis. It is not possible therefore to produce them by the gravity control elements generally used in marine gyro compasses.

Figure 1.42 shows the projection of the gyro spin axis onto the northern horizon, the axis horizontal and pointing to the east of north. The gyro is in north latitude. The north end of the spin axis will drift to the east at a rate given by 15′ sine latitude per minute. That end will also tilt upwards at a rate given by 15′ cosine latitude · sine azimuth per minute. A precession of the north end to the west equal to the drifting, and a precession of the north end downwards equal to the tilting will secure the spin axis in this direction relative to the meridian.

Because of the movement of the craft, which may change course, speed, or latitude, the correcting precessions may not be exactly correct at any given time so that the axis may change direction slowly. The direction indicated must be monitored therefore at regular intervals. Any deviation from the chosen reference direction may be corrected manually. Note that if the axis is placed in the meridian then only the drift will require compensation as the tilting will be zero.

An explanation of the operation of the Arma Brown compass in the directional mode is given in the chapter devoted to that compass.

CHAPTER 2

SPERRY GYROCOMPASSES

2.1 Introduction

Sperry Marine Systems, a division of Sperry Rand Limited now produce a wide range of gyroscopic compasses of varying degree of sophistication. They supply gyros to the USA and NATO fleets as well as to the Admiralty. The present range of commercial gyrocompasses stem from three quarters of a century of experience and development from the original Sperry gyrocompass produced in 1911. From the commercial range two types of compass are described here, the Sperry Mark 20, and the more compact S.R. 120 and S.R. 100 range.

2.2 The Sperry Mark 20

This compass is, by modern standards, of large construction and is one of the few compasses in use today whose constituent parts can clearly be seen when in operation. It is ideal therefore for description for the student of gyrocompasses. Although this mark has been superseded by the latest range of miniaturised compasses, many are still in use throughout the fleets of the world. Basically it is of the conventional Sperry design but includes features which were new innovations when the mark was first introduced in 1961.

2.3 Construction of the Mark 20—The Sensitive Element

The following description should be clarified by reference to figure 2.1.

The sensitive element of a compass is that part of the compass which when touched will transmit a torque to the rotor and hence disturb the compass from its settled position. In the Mark 20 the sensitive element comprises:

    i. the rotor and rotor case with its attachments,
    ii. the vertical ring and its attachments.

The rotor is of 6·8 kg weight and of 13·9 cm diameter. At operating speed it is driven at 12 000 r.p.m. The rotor carries the windings of a three phase induction motor, the stator windings being on the inside of the rotor case. The rotor is driven by induction about its spin axis which is housed in bearings in the north and south ends of the rotor case. The case is airtight and a partial vacuum is created inside it.

Integral with the rotor case casting is a horizontal platform on top of the rotor case called the support frame. This carries various constituent parts of the compass to be described later. The rotor, rotor case and support frame are supported within the vertical ring by a wire suspension which hangs from the top of the vertical ring with its lower end attached to the top of the support frame. This connection is adjustable to extract any twist in the wire suspension. The vertical ring surrounds the rotor casing in the east–west plane, that is in the plane of the rotor. Its upper end, from which the wire suspension is hung, extends upwards in the shape of an A. This section of the vertical ring is called the A-bracket and carries various constituent parts of the compass to be described later.

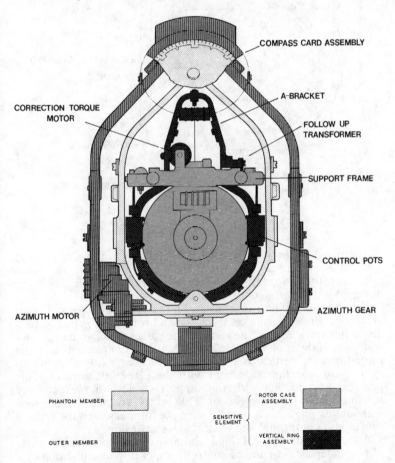

FIG. 2.1(a)   Principle elements of the Mark XX gyro compass.

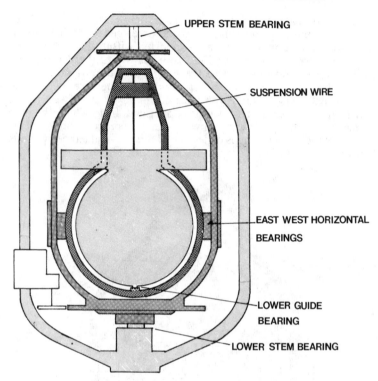

FIG. 2.1(b)   Simplified diagram of principal elements of Mark XX.

The plane of the vertical ring is maintained in the plane of the rotor by the lower guide bearing. This bearing supports no weight from the rotor casing but bears only laterally on a spindle projecting down from the bottom of the rotor casing.

Freedom in azimuth is afforded by the vertical suspension wire and lower guide bearing, as the rotor and rotor case is free to turn about this vertical axis. The vertical ring passes through the east and west ends of the support frame but without any contact with it. If the rotor turns the vertical ring is made to turn with it (see follow up system), to maintain alignment with the plane of the rotor. This prevents any contact with the support frame and prevents any twisting of the wire suspension. This follow up must be achieved without any physical contact between the rotor case and the vertical ring other than through the vertical axis suspension.

Attached to the vertical ring is the control element which consists of two independent pairs of control pots, each pair consisting of a north and a south pot connected by a pipe between their bottoms and an air pipe between their tops. Each pair of pots contains two ounces of mercury. The pots are attached to the vertical ring, one pair to the east of the north–south spin axis and the other pair to the west. Mercury flows by gravity when the element tilts giving a top heavy effect.

2.4 The Phantom Ring

The sensitive element is suspended within the phantom ring by connections in the east–west horizontal axis between the vertical ring and the phantom ring. The plane of the phantom ring coincides with the plane of the vertical ring when the latter is upright but the vertical ring and hence the whole sensitive element, including the vertical axis, has freedom to tilt about this horizontal east–west axis.

The phantom ring drives the compass card assembly. This assembly which is carried by the outer member (see section 2.5), will be described later, but in principle the compass card may be thought of as being a conventional horizontal compass card rigidly mounted on top of the phantom ring. As the phantom ring and the vertical ring are coplanar in the east–west plane when the compass is settled, the phantom ring will define the positions of the graduations of the scale of the compass card.

At the bottom of the phantom ring is the azimuth gear which is a horizontal gear wheel fixed to the phantom, by means of which the phantom ring may be driven in azimuth. Note that if the phantom turns then so also must the vertical ring through the east–west horizontal connection.

2.5 The Outer Member

The phantom is supported within the outer member in bearings in the vertical axis such that the phantom may turn in azimuth within the outer member. The bearings are referred to as the lower stem bearing and the upper stem bearing. The outer member turns with the ship and always remains in the ship's athwartships plane, while the phantom with the compass card attached remains stationary with respect to the meridian. The phantom may be driven in azimuth through its azimuth gear by the azimuth motor which is attached to the outer member. The azimuth motor drives the phantom and therefore the sensitive element in azimuth, relative to the outer member.

Power supplies are conveyed to the sensitive element through an assembly of slip rings in the lower stem bearing.

The compass card assembly is carried on the top of the outer member but is driven by the movement of the phantom ring relative to the outer member. It may help in understanding the basic principles of the operation of the compass if initially the compass card is thought of as being attached to the phantom as a conventional horizontal compass card. (This is a feature of the Mark XIV which was superseded by the Mark 20.) The actual compass card assembly arrangement will be described later.

The outer member is supported in gimbals which are damped for roll and pitch and mounted in shock proof mountings. These will be described later but we are now in a position to describe the operation of the compass.

2.6   Control of the Gyro

The control element, which is attached to the vertical ring, consists of two independent pairs of pots, each pair containing two ounces of mercury, which flows between north and south pots when the sensitive element tilts, giving a top heavy effect (see section 2.3). The action of the control element is, when the rotor and rotor case tilts out of the horizontal, the vertical ring tilts with it, due to the connection at the lower guide bearing. The control element which is attached to the vertical ring therefore tilts also and mercury flows to the low side. This north or south heaviness creates a torque on the vertical ring about the horizontal east–west axis, which is transmitted to the rotor via the lower guide bearing. This creates a precession in azimuth (see section 1.10). The precession must be to the west when the north end of the spin axis tilts upwards, and to the east when that end tilts downwards. The design of the control element is such that the period of the undamped ellipse in the Mark 20 is 113 minutes.

2.7   Damping of the Gyro

Damping of the ellipse is obtained by a small damping weight of 17 grams placed on the support frame in the plane of the rotor and offset to the west of the vertical axis. The action of such a damping weight has been described in section 1.17, where it was explained that when the 'nominal' vertical axis tilts out of the vertical due to the tilt of the rotor (see section 2.6), a torque about the nominal vertical axis is produced. This gives a precession in tilt, the direction of which depends upon the direction of the tilt, and the magnitude of which is proportional to the tilt. The effect of this precession in tilt was described in section 1.19.

2.8   The Follow Up System

It has been shown that the rotor and the rotor casing has freedom to turn in azimuth about the vertical suspension axis, and that the sensitive element has freedom to tilt about the horizontal east–west axis. Thus it has the properties of a free gyroscope. Furthermore there is control and damping so that the rotor will settle in the meridian. There must however be provision to cause the vertical ring and the phantom ring to maintain alignment with the plane of the rotor. This is necessary to prevent any twist forming in the vertical wire suspension when the rotor turns, as this would exert a torque on the rotor. Also, as the compass card is attached to the phantom (theoretically), this provision for the vertical ring and phantom ring to follow the rotor will transmit the directional reference provided by the rotor to the compass card. This follow up is achieved as follows.

Alignment between the rotor case and the vertical ring is sensed by the E-shaped transformer. This consists of a transformer with its windings on the arms of an E-shaped soft iron core. The primary windings are on the central arm of the E and there are two secondary windings on the outer arms. These secondary windings are in series and wound in opposing directions. The outputs from the secondaries will therefore be equal and of opposite phase and will cancel giving a zero output. This E-shaped transformer is attached to the east side of the support frame. On the A bracket of the vertical ring is an armature which is close to the E-shaped core and symmetrical with the secondary windings when the vertical ring is correctly aligned with the rotor case. This arrangement of E-shaped transformer and armature is shown in figure 2.2. In this position the output of the secondary coils is zero. If the rotor now turns causing a displacement between the support frame of the rotor casing and the vertical ring, the armature will no longer be symmetrical with the two secondary windings. A greater current will be induced in the secondary winding towards which the armature is displaced, due to the soft iron flux path as opposed to the partial air path for the other secondary. The two secondary currents will only partially cancel and an output will appear across the two secondary coils. The phase of this output will depend upon the direction of displacement of the armature. In this

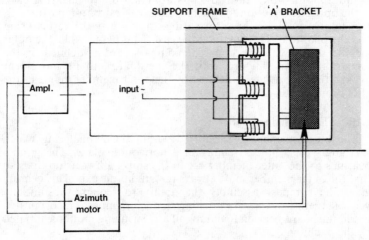

Fig. 2.2

way an electrical signal is obtained which is proportional to the displacement between the rotor case and the vertical ring and whose phase depends on the direction of the displacement.

This signal is amplified by the follow up amplifier and used to drive the azimuth motor. This turns the phantom ring within the outer member and hence the vertical ring through the east–west horizontal connection, in such a direction as to restore the alignment with the rotor. When alignment is achieved the signal will go to zero and the azimuth motor will stop. The sensing device is very sensitive so that the vertical ring follows the movement of the rotor almost instantaneously.

The compass card turns with the phantom and thus indicates the movement of the rotor.

2.9   Action of the Compass when the Vessel Alters Course

Initially the rotor plane, the vertical ring and the phantom ring will be in the east–west plane, with the rotor axis settled in the meridian. The outer member is in the athwartships plane of the vessel, and if the vessel is initially heading north this will be in the same plane as the phantom and the vertical ring. If the vessel now alters course the rotor and the rotor casing will, due to the gyroscopic inertia, remain in the meridian. The outer member will turn with the ship and, due to the connection through the azimuth motor drive to the phantom azimuth gear, the phantom and the vertical ring will be turned with the ship, causing a displacement between the rotor case and the vertical ring. Immediately a displacement occurs however a signal is obtained from the E-shaped transformer which drives the azimuth motor which turns the phantom and the vertical ring back in the opposite direction to the ship's turn, to restore alignment with the support frame of the rotor casing. In this way the vertical ring and the phantom ring remain in the east–west plane, while the outer member turns with the ship. The compass card as defined by the phantom remains aligned with the meridian, and its movement against the lubber line as defined by the outer member indicates the alteration of course.

2.10   The Gimbal Support

The outer member is supported within the gimbal ring which surrounds the whole assembly in a horizontal plane. The gimbal bearings to the outer member are in the ship's athwartships axis so that the outer member must always remain in this axis. This bearing gives the compass assembly the ability to remain substantially vertical against the vessel's pitching. A pitch damper is incorporated in the starboard bearing to damp out any swinging motions initiated by the pitching.

The gimbal ring is supported in bearings in the ship's fore and aft axis, by the support brackets, so that the compass can remain substantially vertical against the roll of the ship. The for'd bearing incorporates a roll damper to damp out any swinging motion initiated by the ship's roll. The support brackets are free to slide up or down on vertical posts projecting upwards from the main binnacle housing. The weight of the support brackets and hence the whole of the compass assembly is taken by long helical springs fitted around each post. These damp out the downwards movement of the

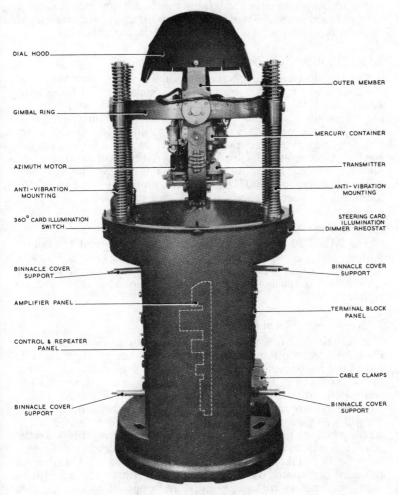

DIAL HOOD

OUTER MEMBER

GIMBAL RING

MERCURY CONTAINER

AZIMUTH MOTOR

TRANSMITTER

ANTI-VIBRATION MOUNTING

ANTI-VIBRATION MOUNTING

360° CARD ILLUMINATION SWITCH

STEERING CARD ILLUMINATION DIMMER RHEOSTAT

BINNACLE COVER SUPPORT

BINNACLE COVER SUPPORT

AMPLIFIER PANEL

TERMINAL BLOCK PANEL

CONTROL & REPEATER PANEL

CABLE CLAMPS

BINNACLE COVER SUPPORT

BINNACLE COVER SUPPORT

Fig. 2.3   Mark XX gyro compass (covers removed)—port side view.

support brackets. Above the support bracket short helical springs are fitted over the posts and these absorb the upwards movement of the support brackets. These provide an anti-vibration mounting.

2.11   The Compass Card Assembly

The compass card assembly is carried on top of the outer member and comprises two compass cards each with a gear train which meshes with the drive gear on the top of the phantom ring. A 360° direct reading compass card faces for'd, and an enlarged scale compass card faces aft for steering purposes. Both cards are turned by the rotation of the phantom ring within the outer member.

2.12   The Binnacle

The binnacle encloses the compass unit and its mounting, and contains a lower section beneath the compass which houses the switch panels for the compass and repeaters, and the amplifiers for the follow up system and the repeater transmission system. The terminal block panel is situated on the after side in the lower binnacle and serves as a convenient connection point for all electrical services. Electrical inputs are derived from the motor alternator, the motor of which is driven by the ship's mains supply. The alternator generates outputs at 400 Hz to provide supplies for the rotor, the follow up transformer, amplifiers, and error correction system.

2.13   Correction of Errors

The Mark 20 is corrected for damping error and for course latitude and speed error by application of a small torque about the vertical axis, to give a precession in tilt. This creates a new equilibrium with the axis in the meridian. The torque is applied by the correction torque motor.

2.13(a)   Correction of Damping Error

It has been shown that the damping error arises because of a damping precession in tilt which is created when the spin axis tilts out of the horizontal (see section 1.23). The axis must settle with a tilt of the north end upwards in north latitude and downwards in south latitude, in order to obtain a precession in azimuth which is required to compensate for the drift due to the earth's rotation. This tilt will also give a damping precession in tilt which will be downwards when the north end is tilted upwards and upwards when the north end is tilted downwards. To balance this precession in tilt there must be an equal precession in the opposite direction. Uncorrected this must be acquired by settling out of the meridian where the tilting due to the earth's rotation is equal and opposite to the damping precession. Thus the axis will settle to the east of the meridian in north latitude and to the west of the meridian in south latitude. The displacement from the meridian constitutes the damping error.

In the Mark 20 a torque about the vertical axis is provided by the correction torque motor. This gives the precession in tilt which equals and opposes the damping precession. In effect it therefore replaces the tilting, thus obviating the need to settle out of the meridian to acquire the tilting. The axis will settle in the meridian with a slight tilt which does not affect the operation of the compass.

The damping precession which must be compensated for by this correction torque is proportional to the tilt (see section 1.18). The tilt in its turn is proportional to the drift in that particular latitude, as it is to compensate for the drift that the tilt is necessary. The drift varies as the sine of the latitude so that the correction torque applied must also be proportional to the sine of the latitude.

2.13(b)   Correction of Course Latitude and Speed Error (Steaming Error)

In the Mark 20 this error is eliminated at source (see section 1.27). The error was introduced due to the false tilting of the spin axis caused by the vessel's movement across the earth's surface in the north or south direction. The north–south component of the vessel's speed is given by $v \cdot \cos$ course, and this will be the rate of tilting per hour due to this cause. A small torque is applied about the vertical axis to give a precession in tilt equal to $v \cdot \cos$ course but in the opposite direction. This will be downwards when the vessel is steaming north and upwards when the vessel is steaming south.

Note that both errors are corrected by a torque about the vertical axis. The correction of both errors may therefore be achieved by one combined torque, and this is applied by the correction torque motor.

2.14   Error Correction Signals

The correction torque motor requires an electrical signal which has components proportional to the cosine of the course, the speed and the sine of the latitude, in order to correct for the course latitude and speed error and the damping error.

A signal which is proportional to the cosine of the course is provided by the cosine resolver. This is situated at the top of the outer member and phantom ring. Stator coils attached to the outer member have signals induced in them by transformer action from a primary rotor coil, fed by single phase a.c., and attached to the top of the phantom ring. The rotor will therefore rotate with respect to the secondaries (stator coils) when the vessel alters course, which causes the outer member to rotate around the phantom and sensitive element. The output from the stator coils must be maximum when the vessel is heading north or south, and zero when the vessel is heading east or west, varying as the cosine of the course angle.

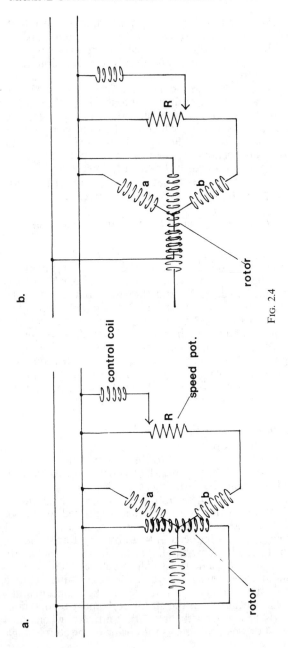

FIG. 2.4

The stator windings on the outer member consist of three star connected windings as shown in figure 2.4. With the ship on north the rotor is aligned as shown in 2.4(a). The voltage across the load resistor R will be the voltage across the coils a and b, which will be a maximum with the rotor aligned thus. When the vessel is heading east or west the rotor is aligned as shown in 2.4(b). The voltage across the load resistor R will be zero. With the vessel on south the rotor will be aligned as shown in 2.4(a). The output will again be maximum but of opposite phase to that with the vessel on north.

The speed potentiometer is controlled by the navigators setting of the vessel's speed. With the setting in the zero position as shown in figure 2.4(a), the signal passed to the correction torque motor will be zero, irrespective of the voltage across the cosine resolver. With the speed setting as shown in 2.4(b), the full voltage from the cosine resolver will be presented to the correction motor. This signal is therefore proportional to the cosine of the course and to the speed. This signal corrects for the course and speed error.

A second signal is obtained from the potentiometer controlled by the navigators setting of the latitude. The output of this is proportional to the sine of the latitude. This signal corrects for the damping error.

2.14(a)   The Correction Torque Motor

The error correction signals are applied to the correction torque motor whose purpose is to create a torque on the rotor which causes a precession in tilt. This precession is the resultant of the two precessions in tilt, described in section 2.13, which are required to correct for damping error and steaming error. The correction motor is a two phase torque motor. A reference phase winding is fed with a single phase a.c., while the control winding receives the error correction signal. The windings are carried on the A bracket of the vertical ring with the axis of the coils aligned parallel to the north–south axis. A copper covered armature passes through the centre of the coils also parallel to the north–south axis but carried on the support frame of the rotor case. Currents induced in the copper armature produce a longitudinal force on the armature, that is a force in the north–south direction, which is transmitted to the rotor through the case and the spin axis bearings. As the armature is out of the vertical axis a torque about the vertical axis results and the required precession in tilt is produced.

This precession in tilt eliminates the 'false' tilting due to the vessel's north–south velocity, and opposes the damping precession at the settling position (see section 2.13). The result is a new equilibrium position with the spin axis in the meridian but with a slight tilt, sufficient to give a control precession equal to the drift. The equilibrium position for the settled compass is shown in figure 2.5(a) and (b).

D

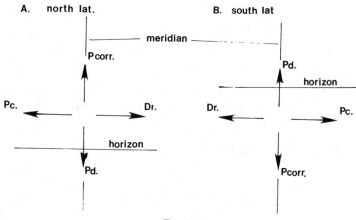

Fig. 2.5

2.15   Transmission to Repeaters

The transmission system transmits rotation of the phantom and sensitive element, within the outer member, to remote repeaters. Thus once the repeaters are set to indicate the ship's head, this heading information is maintained. The transmission system consists of the transmitter, mounted on the master compass, the transmission amplifiers, and the repeater motors which are geared to the repeater cards.

The transmission motor is a synchro transmitter in the form of a

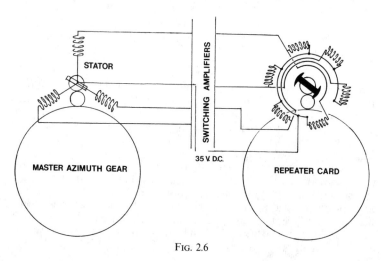

Fig. 2.6

laminated I-shaped rotor which is driven through the intermediate gearing between the azimuth motor and the azimuth gear. Thus when the phantom and sensitive element turn within the outer member in the follow up sequence of the master compass, the transmitter rotor turns also. The rotor rotates inside a six pole, star connected stator winding (see figure 2.6). As the rotor turns, lining up in turn with each of the stator coils, increases in the current flowing in the stator windings are used to activate three switching amplifier circuits, each one of which is connected to a set of coils in the receiver motor. Each set of coils consists of two coils in parallel. The effect of rotating the transmitter rotor is to produce a rotating magnetic field in the receiver stator as each pair of coils is energised in turn. The rotor armature in the receiver motor will turn to align with this magnetic field, thus reproducing the rotation of the transmitter. The receiver rotor is geared to the compass repeater card, the gearing obviously being designed to produce a one degree rotation of the repeater card for each degree rotation of the master compass.

2.16 The S.R. 120/130 Gyrocompass

The trend in modern gyrocompasses is in general towards the small compact or miniaturised compass. The S.R. range of Sperry compasses is in many respects a miniaturised version of the Sperry Mark 20, although there are differences in the details of construction of the two compasses. The S.R. range is identical with the E.S. range of compasses produced by the Japanese TKS Company Ltd.

2.17 The Sensitive Element

The sensitive element consists of the rotor and rotor case and its attachments, and the vertical ring and its attachments. The rotor is of 110 mm diameter and forms the rotor of a three phase induction motor, whose stator windings are on the inside of the rotor case. The rotor spin axis is supported within the rotor case in ball bearings in the north and south ends of the case. The rotor rotates at slightly less than 12 000 r.p.m. when a supply of three phase 110V at 400 Hz is connected to the stator windings.

The rotor case is supported within the vertical ring which surrounds the rotor case in the east–west plane, that is in the plane of the rotor. The suspension is by means of a six strand stainless steel suspension wire, carefully adjusted to be free of any torsion or twisting. The top of the suspension wire is attached to the top of the vertical ring which extends upwards to form the suspension frame in the manner of the A bracket in the Mark 20. The lower end of the suspension wire is attached to the top of a stem which projects upwards from the top of the rotor case in the vertical axis. This stem is laterally supported by a guide bearing in the vertical ring, as is a similar stem projecting downwards from the bottom of the rotor

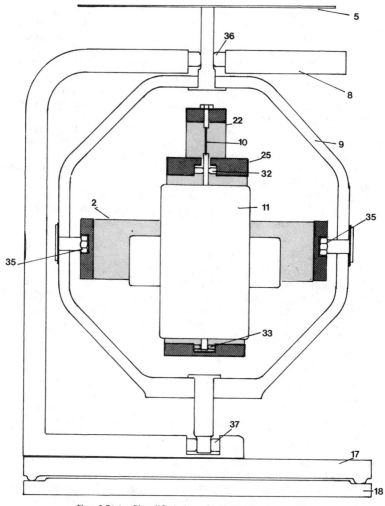

FIG. 2.7(a)   Simplified view of S.R. 120 from west side.

Key to figures 2.7(a), (b), (c) and (d).
1. Shock absorbing mountings.
2. Horizontal ring.
3. Level.
4. Illumination.
5. Compass card.
6. Fuse holder.
7. Slip ring assembly.

8. Support frame.
9. Phantom ring.
10. Suspension wire.
11. Rotor case.
12. Rotor.
13. Control element.
14. Damper.
15. Ball bearing (Lower stem bearing).

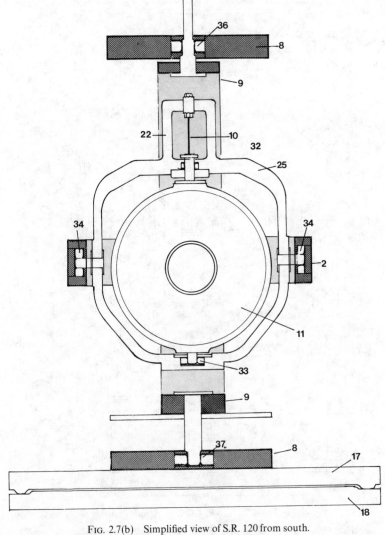

FIG. 2.7(b) Simplified view of S.R. 120 from south.

16. Azimuth motor.
17. Upper base plate.
18. Lower base plate.
19. Synchro transmitter.
20. Damping weight.

21. Binnacle cover.
22. Suspension frame.
23. Follow up transformer primary.
24. Follow up transformer secondary.
25. Vertical ring.

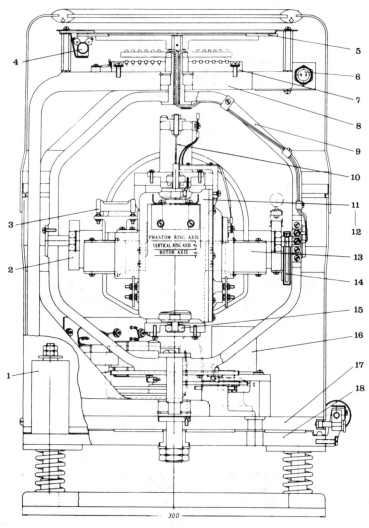

PHANTOM RING AXIS
VERTICAL RING AXIS
ROTOR AXIS

FIG. 2.7(c) S.R. 120 viewed from west.

Key to figures 2.7(a–d)—*contd.*
26. Binnacle.
27. Follow up amplifier.
28. Variable resistor.
29. Latitude corrector control.
30. Upper latitude scale.
31. Lower latitude scale.

32. Upper guide bearing.
33. Lower guide bearing.
34. East–west horizontal bearing.
35. North–south horizontal bearing
    (Horizontal ring to phantom).
36. Upper stem bearing.
37. Lower stem bearing.

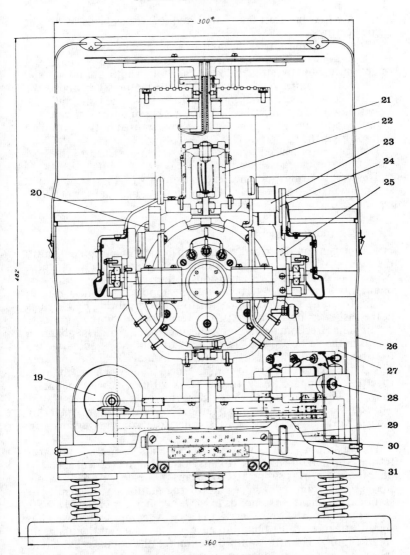

FIG. 2.7(d)   S.R. 120 viewed from south.

casing. These guide bearings take no weight but maintain the rotor case in the vertical axis of the vertical ring and maintains the vertical ring in the plane of the rotor when the rotor tilts. The weight of the rotor and case is taken only by the wire suspension. The rotor and rotor case thus has freedom to turn about a vertical axis within the guide bearings.

The vertical ring carries the control element which consists of two pairs of pots each pair consisting of a north and a south pot interconnected between their lower ends for free flow of liquid, and between their upper ends to equalise the air pressure above the liquid. The liquid used is of high density and is called 'daifloil'. The liquid flows by gravity when the rotor case and vertical ring tilt, giving a top heavy effect. The torque is transmitted to the rotor case and rotor via the guide bearings.

Damping is produced by a damping weight attached to the west side of the rotor case (see section 1.17).

The vertical ring and the rotor casing carry the primary and secondary coils respectively, of the follow up transformer (see section 2.20).

2.18   The Phantom Element

The suspension described so far is, in basic principle, identical to the Sperry Mark 20. The most noticeable difference between these two compasses is in the suspension of the vertical ring within the phantom element. The vertical ring is supported within a ring in the horizontal plane and connected to the vertical ring by bearings in the east–west horizontal axis. The vertical ring and the rotor case within it has freedom to tilt about this horizontal axis. The phantom ring is in the vertical plane outside the horizontal ring and attached to it by bearings in the north–south horizontal axis. The phantom ring is thus held in the north–south vertical plane when the compass is settled. (Compare this with the Mark 20 in which the phantom ring is attached directly to the vertical ring in the east–west plane). The south bearing between the phantom ring and the horizontal ring incorporates an oil damper to stabilise the compass against the ship's roll or pitch.

The phantom ring carries two stem shafts projecting upwards from its top and downwards from its bottom, in the vertical axis. The phantom element is supported by means of these stem shafts within the support frame which is part of the stationary element. The stationary element corresponds to the outer member of the Mark 20. The upper stem shaft also serves to carry the compass card which is rigidly attached to the phantom element, the plane of the phantom ring defining the north–south direction for the compass card. The lower extremity of the phantom ring at the lower stem shaft, carries the azimuth gear, this being part of the follow up system.

2.19   The Stationary Element

The stationary element is that part of the compass which can be considered fixed to the ship, that is the parts which will turn with the ship during an alteration of course. It consists of the main supporting frame, base plates and binnacle with various attachments.

The supporting frame holds the ball bearings in which the upper and lower stem shafts of the phantom ring are supported, and consists of a vertical support on the northern side of the compass with an upper arm projecting horizontally to carry the upper stem bearing and a lower arm to carry the lower stem bearing. The lower arm is fixed to the base.

The base consists of two plates, the upper and the lower plates. The two plates are joined by a shaft through their centres such that the two plates may be rotated around the shaft relative to each other. This forms part of the error correction system (see section 2.21). The lower base plate is carried on a shock absorbing mounting the bottom plate of which is secured to the ship. The upper base plate carries the azimuth motor, the follow up amplifier, and the repeater transmitter.

The whole is enclosed in the binnacle cover which has a glass top for viewing the master compass card directly.

2.20   The Follow Up System

The follow up system maintains the vertical ring in the same plane as the rotor. The rotor and rotor casing, we have seen, have freedom to turn about the vertical axis (suspension wire), within the guide bearings of the vertical ring. The vertical ring must follow the rotor as the spin axis seeks and settles in the meridian, and must remain

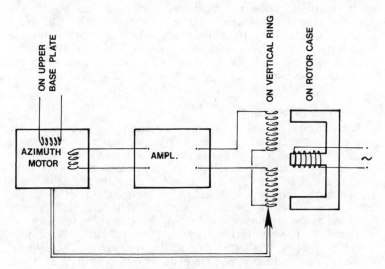

FIG. 2.8   Follow up system of S.R. 120.

aligned with the rotor when the ship alters course, in order that the wire suspension does not twist and apply a torque to the rotor. The follow up transformer senses any misalignment between the rotor case and the vertical ring. It consists of a primary coil attached to the east side of the rotor casing, and a secondary coil attached to the vertical ring such that the two coils are centrally aligned when the vertical ring is correctly aligned with the rotor case. The two halves of the secondary are wound in opposite directions (see figure 2.8), so that the currents induced in two halves cancel each other when they are equal, that is when alignment is correct. Misalignment will cause the currents induced in the two halves to be unequal, and hence to produce an output across the secondary which is proportional to the misalignment and of phase dependent upon the direction of misalignment. This transformer performs the same function as the E-shaped transformer on the Mark 20.

The output from the follow up transformer is amplified by the follow up amplifier and drives the azimuth motor which is fixed to the stationary element. The motor drives the azimuth gear which is attached to the phantom element in order to turn the phantom ring relative to the stationary element. The vertical ring must also turn with the phantom ring through the connection via the horizontal ring. The phantom and the vertical ring are therefore driven until the vertical ring is in alignment with the rotor casing, seeking a zero output from the follow up transformer. The vertical ring is thus maintained in the east–west plane, that is the plane of the rotor when the axis is settled, and the phantom in the north–south plane. The north–south direction of the compass card, as defined by the phantom ring is in this way maintained in the meridian. The ship's head is indicated by the lubber line which is marked on the stationary element (support frame), in the ship's fore and aft axis. An alteration of course is indicated by the rotation of the phantom within the stationary element which produces an angular movement of the compass card against the lubber line.

2.21   Error Correction

The two operational errors, the damping error (latitude error), and the course latitude and speed error (steaming error), are not corrected in the S.R. compasses. The spin axis will settle out of the meridian by an amount equal to the algebraic sum of the two errors (see sections 1.24 and 1.25). The effect of the damping error (latitude error) can be removed however, by an arrangement by which the lubber line is shifted by an amount equal to the error. This is achieved by the arrangement of the upper and lower base plates (see section 2.19). The compass is carried on the upper base plate, and the lower base plate is secured to the ship mounting. The latitude corrector rotates the upper base plate with the compass attached, relative to the lower base plate. The lubber line is therefore offset from the ship's fore and aft line by the amount of the error, although the direction of the spin axis will be unaffected.

The correction is set in the compass by the latitude corrector knob. This moves a scale of latitude attached to the upper base plate against a scale of latitude attached to the lower base plate, the two scales being of unequal length. The appropriate latitude for the ship is matched across the two scales by the latitude corrector knob.

The course latitude and speed error (steaming error) is not corrected on this compass but must be allowed for in the use of the compass as a compass error in the usual way. The amount of the error may be obtained from a graph supplied with the operator's manual, or it may be calculated from the approximate formula given and derived in section 1.25.

2.22 Transmission to Repeaters

Transmission to remote repeaters is done by the inductive transmitter, the switching amplifiers, and the receiver step motors which drive the repeater cards.

The inductive transmitter is attached to the upper base plate of the stationary element of the master compass, and is driven by the azimuth gear of the phantom element. Any rotation of the phantom ring within the stationary element during the follow up procedure, is therefore sensed by the transmitter and automatically transmitted to the repeaters, which rotate in sympathy with the phantom ring and master compass card.

The inductive transmitter consists of a primary coil which is supplied with 110V a.c. at 400 Hz. The star-shaped rotor is situated within the primary coil, the magnetic field of which induces an alternating magnetic field in those arms of the star-shaped rotor which are lined up with the axis of the primary coil as illustrated in figure 2.9. The arrangement of three pairs of secondary coils as shown around the rotor means that there will be alternating currents induced in the secondary coils, the magnitude of which will depend upon the alignment of the star-shaped rotor with the pole pieces of the secondary coils. With the rotor aligned as shown in figure 2.9(a) there will be maximum alternating current induced in the pairs S2 as the alternating magnetic field will be concentrated through the pole pieces of S2 through the star-shaped rotor. There will be a minimum alternating current induced in the two pairs S1 and S3.

If the phantom ring now rotates through $\frac{1}{3}°$ the gearing from the azimuth gear will rotate the star-shaped rotor by 30°. It will then be aligned as shown in figure 2.9(b). The magnetic field will be concentrated through the pole pieces of the secondary coils S3, and maximum current is induced in S3 and minimum currents in S1 and S2. A further rotation of the phantom of $\frac{1}{3}°$ will turn the rotor to the position shown in figure 2.9(c). The magnetic field of the primary coil is now concentrated mainly in the other arms of the rotor as

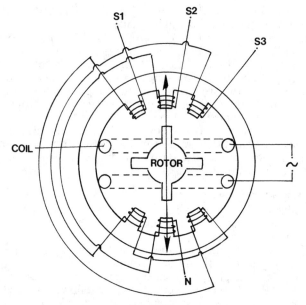

FIG. 2.9(a)

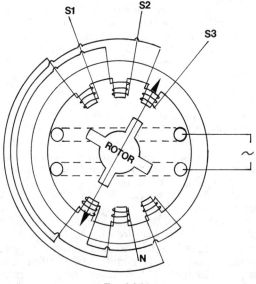

FIG. 2.9(b)

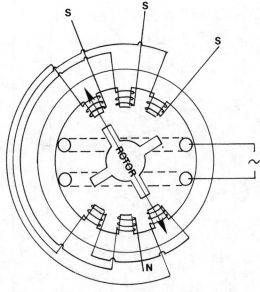

FIG. 2.9(c)

these are now more closely aligned with the axis of the coil. The field is therefore concentrated through the pole pieces of the secondary coils S1, and maximum current is induced in these coils, with minimum currents induced in the coils S2 and S3. A further rotation of the phantom by $\frac{1}{3}°$ will restore the original condition when maximum currents were induced in the secondaries S2.

The a.c. currents and voltage induced in each pair of coils will vary as shown in figure 2.10, which is a graph of voltage against angular rotation of the star-shaped rotor and the phantom ring.

The amplitude of the a.c. voltages across the transmitter secondary coils after rectification and smoothing are used to control transistorised switching circuits. The magnitude of the input derived from the transmitter secondary coils determines whether a transistor will conduct or not and this transistor switch is used to control whether current from a 35 volt d.c. (S.R. 120) or a 70 volt d.c. (S.R. 130) supply will flow through a pair of coils in the receiver motor. There is one such circuit for each of the three pairs of coils in the transmitter each controlling one of three pairs of coils in the receiver. The sensitivity of the switching circuits are adjusted such that the d.c. current to the receiver coils is switched on over a 45° rotation of the star-shaped rotor in the transmitter, that is for $22\frac{1}{2}°$ on either side of the maximum induced voltage in the secondaries (see figure 2.10).

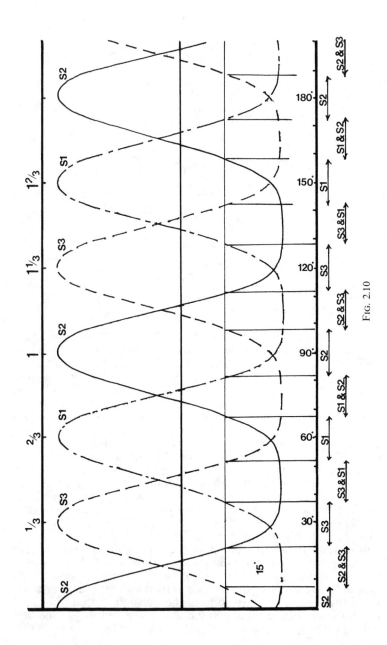

FIG. 2.10

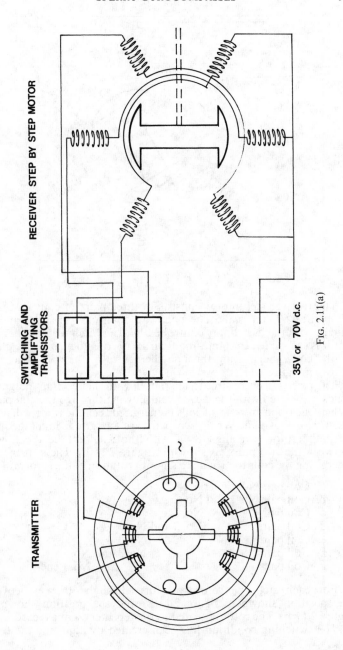

RECEIVER STEP BY STEP MOTOR

SWITCHING AND AMPLIFYING TRANSISTORS

35V or 70V d.c.

TRANSMITTER

Fig. 2.11(a)

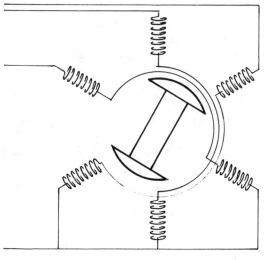

Fig. 2.11(b)

The receiver step motor consists of three pairs of coils mutually aligned at 60° intervals. The pairs are connected in series and in circuit with the d.c. supply controlled by the switching amplifiers. A rotor is suspended to rotate about an axis perpendicular to the plane of the coils and passing through the centre of the coil pattern as shown in figure 2.11.

The receiver rotor is free to align itself with the resultant magnetic fields associated with the d.c. current flowing through the coil pairs. When one opposing pair of coils is energised then the rotor will align itself with that pair. When two pairs are energised simultaneously then the rotor will align itself with the resultant field half way between the two pairs, as shown in figure 2.11(b). The sequence of energising the coils to produce a smooth rotation of the rotor will be:

 a. Coil pair No. 1 energised
 b. Coil pair No. 1 and No. 2
 c. Coil pair   No. 2
 d. Coil pairs No. 2 and No. 3
 e. Coil pair   No. 3
 f. Coil pairs   No. 3 and No. 1
 g. Coil pair   No. 1 energised

For each step the rotor will turn through 30°, i.e. between the position shown in figure 2.11(a) and the position shown in figure 2.11(b). The rotor is geared to the repeater compass card.

The switching condition has been created by adjusting the transistor switches to conduct over a rotation of the transmitter star-shaped rotor of 45°. This is illustrated in figure 2.10. The switches will conduct and energise the coils in the receiver when the a.c. voltage in the secondary coils of the transmitter rise above the level indicated in the figure. This means that there will be a sequence in which first coils S1 are energised, followed by S1 and S2, followed by S2 only, followed by S2 and S3, followed by S3 only followed by S3 and S1, and so on. Figure 2.10 shows that these steps will be produced by successive 15° rotations of the transmitter rotor, such rotations being caused by a 1/6th degree rotation of the master compass.

Each of these steps however we have seen to produce a 30° rotation of the rotor in the receiver. This rotor is geared to the repeater compass with a gearing ratio of 180 : 1. Thus for a 30° rotation of the receiver rotor the repeater card will rotate through 30/180° = 1/6th of a degree. This is the same rotation as that of the master compass which initiated it. The repeater card therefore turns at the same rate as the master compass.

The rapid rotation of the transmitter and receiver rotors for a comparatively slow rotation of the compass cards ensures a smooth and instantaneous transmission to the repeaters.

THE SPERRY MARK 37 GYROCOMPASS

2.23 Introduction

The Mark 37 is the latest in the range of Sperry commercial compasses and incorporates a miniaturised design developed for simplicity of construction and reliability. The liquid ballistic common to Sperry compasses is retained with an immersed gyrosphere. A notable feature of the compass is the absence of an external binnacle gimbal suspension, the master compass being integral with the binnacle which is mounted in shock proof mountings directly in a mounting base which is secured to a level surface on the vessel. The errors on intercardinal courses when the vessel inclines in a seaway are minimised by the design of the gyrosphere which floats with neutral buoyancy with a centre of gravity coincident with its centre of buoyancy. This minimises the effect of roll accelerations on the gyrosphere, and the effect of these accelerations on the liquid ballistic is controlled by restricting the flow of oil in the short term period of a roll by the bore of the interconnecting pipes. In this way rolling errors are maintained within tolerable limits under the most severe conditions.

2.24 Construction of the Mark 37—The Sensitive Element

The sensitive element of the mark 37 consists of the gyrosphere which contains the rotor, the vertical ring and their attachments.

The rotor consists of two end bells connected by a rotor shaft. This is supported inside a circular frame with bosses inside to carry the bearings of the rotor which are between the rotor shaft and the end bells. The spin axis of the rotor, perpendicular to the plane of the circular frame will be the north–south axis of the gyro. The circular frame in the east–west axis carries two hemispherical shells, one north and one south to completely enclose the rotor. The circular frame carries stator windings and an aluminium squirrel cage rotor is cast into the rotor shaft, the whole forming an induction motor which spins the rotor at 12 000 r.p.m. The spherical assembly is referred to as the gyrosphere which is sealed, evacuated and partially filled with helium which transfers heat from the rotor through the gyrosphere. The gyrosphere is 6·5 inches in diameter.

The gyrosphere is supported within the vertical ring which surrounds the gyrosphere in the east–west. The connection is through upper and lower bearings in the vertical axis providing freedom for the gyrosphere to turn in azimuth about this axis. (These bearings are comparable to the suspension wire and guide bearings of the Mark 20 and S.R. 120 compasses.) Although the gyrosphere has freedom to turn in azimuth within the vertical ring, in normal operation it maintains a constant alignment with it. A rotation of the gyrosphere relative to the vertical ring will bring stops on the vertical ring into contact with spring stops on the gyrosphere. These stops are irrelevant to the normal operation but will be mentioned with respect to the rapid settling procedure.

The Phantom

The vertical ring is supported within the phantom element through bearings in the horizontal east–west axis providing freedom for the vertical ring and gyrosphere to tilt about this axis. The phantom element is in the form of an inverted fork and is referred to as the phantom yoke, the top of which extends upwards in a stem in the vertical axis. This vertical stem carries the azimuth gear. The phantom yoke and sensitive element are supported by the support plate through four point contact bearings around the vertical stem of the phantom yoke. The support plate is part of the stationary element of the compass which is attached to the vessel and carries the azimuth motor which drives the phantom yoke relative to the support plate through the azimuth gear.

The Binnacle

The support plate is the top plate of the lower binnacle which enclosed the phantom and sensitive elements. This binnacle is filled with a floatation fluid which completely immerses the compass assembly. At correct operating temperature the gyrosphere has neutral buoyancy which relieves the vertical and horizontal bearings of all load leaving them as guide bearings only. This provides a virtually friction free mounting for the sensitive element.

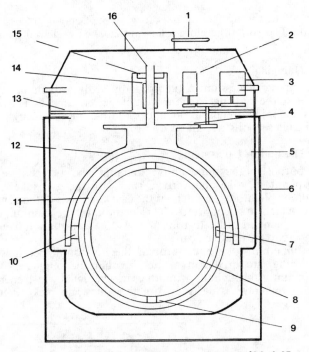

FIG. 2.12   Simplified diagram of main components of Mark 37.

1. Cager lever.
2. Repeater transmitter.
3. Azimuth motor.
4. Azimuth gear.
5. Lower binnacle.
6. Mounting base.
7. Follow up pickoff.
8. Gyrosphere.
9. Vertical axis bearings.
10. Horizontal axis bearings.
11. Vertical ring.
12. Phantom yoke.
13. Support plate.
14. Phantom yoke bearings.
15. Cosine resolver.
16. Compass card drive.

Figure 2.12 shows a simplified diagram of the main constituent parts of the compass.

2.25   Control

The control element consists of a liquid ballistic comprising two tanks attached to the gyrosphere, one north and one south in the rotor spin axis. These are interconnected by small bore tube between their bottoms and an air pipe between their tops forming a sealed unit. The tanks contain a silicone oil which flows by gravity to the low side when the gyrosphere tilts, producing a top heavy type torque about the horizontal axis to give the control precession in azimuth. The rotor therefore spins anticlockwise viewed from the south.

2.26 Damping

A damping precession in tilt is produced by a damping weight attached to the gyrosphere to the west of the vertical axis. The action of this damping weight is identical to that of the Mark 20 as described in sections 1.17 and 2.7.

2.27 The Follow Up System

The purpose of the follow up is to maintain the correct alignment of the phantom yoke and vertical ring with the gyrosphere. The plane of the phantom yoke defines the east–west axis of the compass card to which it is connected. This plane must be maintained in the rotor plane in order to transmit heading information from the gyrosphere to the compass card.

The phantom yoke and, through the horizontal bearings, the vertical ring, are driven in azimuth within the binnacle by the azimuth motor through the azimuth gear. The signal which energises the azimuth motor is derived from the follow up pick off which

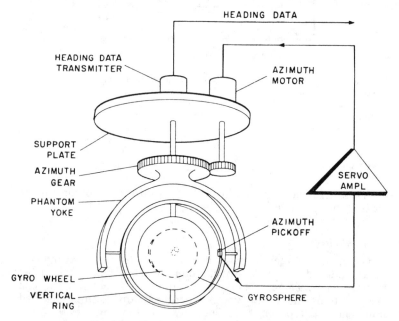

FIG. 2.13 Simplified diagram of follow up control.

senses any misalignment in azimuth between the gyrosphere and the vertical ring. The error signal is proportional to the misalignment and of phase dependent upon the direction of misalignment. The azimuth motor drives the phantom yoke and vertical ring to restore correct alignment and zero error signal.

The sensing device consists of an E–I transformer, the E-shaped core being mounted on the vertical ring with the I armature on the gyrosphere. The operation of this type of pickoff has been explained in section 2.8 with reference to the Mark 20.

The azimuth motor is mounted on the support plate of the binnacle with a drive shaft projecting down into the lower binnacle to engage with the azimuth gear of the phantom yoke. Section 2.9 describes the action of the compass during an alteration of course, which in this respect is identical to that of the Mark 20 and S.R. 120 compasses. Figure 2.13 shows the follow up action.

2.28   The Electronic Control Unit

This bulkhead mounted unit contains the electronic circuitry for conversion of ship's power supply to the 400 Hz 3-phase supply required by the master compass unit. It also houses the follow up amplifier and the compass operating control assembly whose operator controls are located on the front panel. These controls consist of a power switch and indicator lamp, a multi-function 'mode' switch with START, SLEW, AUTO LEVEL, RUN, and RUN/SLEW settings. These will be explained in later sections. There is also a SLEW switch which controls the direction of compass slewing.

2.29   The Transmission Unit

This is a separate bulkhead mounted unit which contains the transmission amplifiers which supply sufficient power to serve up to twelve repeaters. The input from the step transmitter driven by the master compass azimuth drive is amplified and supplied to repeaters through individual switches and fuses which are mounted on the front panel of the unit.

2.30   The Speed and Latitude Compensator Unit

This bulkhead mounted unit contains the speed and latitude potentiometers controlled by the navigators setting and provides the error correction signal (see Correction of Errors).

2.31   Correction of Errors

The Mark 37 is corrected for damping error (latitude error), and course, latitude and speed error (steaming error). Both errors are corrected by application of a torque to produce a precession in tilt. One combined signal therefore corrects for both errors. The principles of the error correction are identical to those for the Mark 20 compass as explained in section 2.13, and need not be repeated here. The combined precession in tilt is caused by the correction torque motor which requires an electrical signal which is proportional to the cosine course and the speed to correct for steaming error, and proportional to the sine of the latitude to correct for damping error.

The correction signal is obtained from a synchro resolver whose stator windings are carried on the binnacle around the vertical stem of the phantom yoke. The operation of such a device has been explained in section 2.14. The cosine function output is modified in the speed and latitude compensator unit by the speed potentiometer set by the operator. This signal is then combined with the signal from the latitude potentiometer again controlled by the operator. The combined signal is input to the correction torque motor.

The torquer has an E-shaped core on whose arms are wound reference windings on the centre arm and control windings on the outer arms, in series. The reference windings are fed with single phase a.c. and the control windings with the error correction signal. The whole constitutes a two phase induction motor with the gyrosphere itself acting as the rotor. A torque is produced on the gyrosphere about the vertical axis which results in the desired precession in tilt. The phase of the control signal, which is determined by the cosine function signal and the latitude signal phase will dictate the direction of the tilting. An analysis of the settling position is given for the Mark 20 in section 1.20 and 2.14.

2.32   Rapid Settling

The settling time of the compass may be reduced by slewing the compass to indicate the ship's head approximately.

The Mark 37 has incorporated in the phantom yoke a means of locking the horizontal axis bearings when the compass is stopped to prevent damage. This device which is called the cager will prevent the vertical ring and gyrosphere from tilting. A cager shaft slides down the vertical stem of the phantom yoke, activated by a lever and cam, the lever being positioned on top of the master compass unit. The cager shaft is spring tensioned. The cager shaft causes the cager to move down until it engages with stops on the vertical ring on either side of the horizontal axis bearings, thus locking the bearings. If the cager is engaged with the compass running the pressure caused by the cager springs against the vertical ring may be used to apply a torque to the sensitive element about the horizontal axis, this resulting in a precession in azimuth. This precession is used to slew the compass when the rotor is running to its settling azimuth.

The compass may be slewed either with the rotor running or with the rotor stopped. With the rotor stopped operation of the mode switch to SLEW disconnects the azimuth motor from the follow up pickoff, and applies a signal the phase of which is determined by the direction in which the slew switch is set. The cager should be engaged. The azimuth motor will now drive the phantom yoke and vertical ring to the desired heading, the gyrosphere being turned with them by the vertical ring stops.

If the gyro is running it is not possible for the azimuth motor to slew the sensitive element directly due to the inertia of the rotor. In this case the RUN/SLEW mode should be selected on the mode switch. The cager should be engaged. The operation of the mode switch disconnects the follow up signal from the azimuth motor and substitutes a signal from the SLEW control. In the absence of a follow up signal the azimuth motor will turn the phantom yoke and vertical ring until the vertical ring stops come into contact with the spring stops on the gyrosphere. The pressure on these stops causes a torque about the vertical axis and the gyrosphere precesses in tilt. This brings pressure on one side of the cager which in preventing any further tilt exerts a torque about the horizontal axis, and this causes the necessary precession in azimuth. The SLEW switch should be released as soon as the compass starts to precess in azimuth, but the pressure of the cager springs maintains the torque and the compass continues to precess. When the desired heading is reached the slew is stopped by uncaging the gyro. The fact that the vertical ring and gyrosphere are a few degrees out of correct alignment is allowed for by stopping the slew 2°–3° past the desired heading. When the mode switch is returned to run the follow up signal will be reconnected to the azimuth motor and will realign the vertical ring. The gyrosphere should be near to its settling position.

2.33 Automatic Levelling

Although the slewing facility may place the spin axis near the meridian, the compass will oscillate away from the meridian again unless the axis has the correct tilt or nearly so for the settling position. The AUTO LEVEL mode is selected after slewing to achieve this. With this mode selected a signal which is derived from the electrolytic level (see section 2.34), is used to control the azimuth motor. The electrolytic level is located on top of the vertical ring and senses any tilt of the sensitive element. The output is an electrical signal proportional to the tilt and of phase dependent on the direction of tilt. The phantom yoke and vertical ring are driven in azimuth and in the absence of any follow up will offset from the gyrosphere and apply a torque about the horizontal axis by the action of the stops. The result is a precession in tilt which will cease when the electrolytic level signal goes to zero, when the axis is horizontal. Some marks of Sperry compasses apply a bias signal to the electrolytic level signal so that it goes to zero with a slight tilt

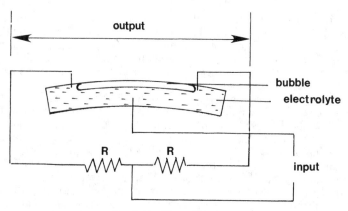

Fig. 2.14   Electrolytic level.

appropriate for the settling position for the vessel's latitude. This signal is derived from the latitude control.

2.34   Electrolytic Level

The electrolytic level consists of a vial of electrolyte with a bubble which centres when the device is level. Three electrodes are immersed in the electrolyte, current flowing between a centre electrode to two outer electrodes through the electrolyte. The two electrolyte paths form a wheatstone bridge with two external load resistors, as shown in figure 2.14.

A single phase a.c. is supplied between the centre electrode and between the two load resistors. With the bubble centred equal currents flow to the two outer electrodes which are therefore at the same potential. The output taken across the two outer electrodes is therefore zero. If the bubble displaces due to a tilt of the sensitive element, the electrolyte resistance on the side to which the bubble displaces increases and unequal currents flow. The outer electrodes are no longer at the same potential and an output results. The phase will reverse if the level tilts the other way.

CHAPTER 3

THE ARMA BROWN GYROCOMPASS

3.1 Introduction

The Arma Brown gyrocompass is a compact miniaturised compass produced by S. G. Brown Ltd., a division of Hawker Siddely. The compass was developed by S. G. Brown and the Bosch Arma Corporation of America and is marketed both in America and in the UK. The compass is unique amongst marine gyrocompasses in that it was originally designed for operation in environments more demanding than those found at sea. The liquid type of control and damping element was replaced by a system less sensitive to the motions and accelerations of the carrying vehicle. The master compass is self contained in a sealed unit designed for ease of operation, to occupy as little space as possible and to require a minimum of operational maintenance.

3.2 The Sensitive Element

This consists of the gyro ball (which contains the rotor), the floating gimbal, and the tank.

The rotor of the Arma Brown consists of a rotor shaft with a 'spinner' at each end. The spinners are the rotors which provide the necessary gyroscopic inertia, and these spin about a spin axis through the rotor shaft. A cross section of the spinners and rotor shaft is of H-section (figure 3.1). The spinners and rotor shaft are supported within an enclosed unit called the gyro ball. This consists of two hollow hemispheres or end bells each enclosing one of the spinners, and connected along the spin axis to enclose the rotor shaft. The rotor shaft is supported in bearings within this central arm of the gyro ball, and is made to spin at just under 12 000 r.p.m. by induction from stator windings on the inside of the central arm of the gyro ball. The sealed gyro ball is filled with helium and the stator windings of the ball supplied with three phase at 400 Hz.

The gyro ball is supported within the sealed tank which is filled, in the space between the ball and the tank with a liquid called fluorolube which has such a density that the gyro ball floats with neutral buoyancy. The ball has therefore freedom to tilt and to turn in azimuth with minimal frictional effects. The ball is located within the tank centrally by two pairs of torsion wires, one pair in the vertical axis and the other pair in the horizontal east–west axis.

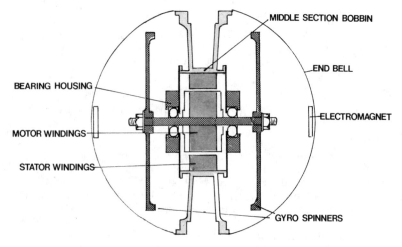

FIG. 3.1   Simplified cross section through gyro ball.

3.3   Connection of the Torsion Wires from Tank to Gyro Ball

The gyro ball is encircled by the primary gimbal which is a square frame which lies in the east–west vertical plane in the annular groove between the two halves of the gyro ball. This may be likened to the vertical ring in a conventional compass. The vertical axis torsion wires connect the inside of the tank at its top and bottom to the outside of the horizontal top and bottom sections of the primary gimbal. The horizontal east–west torsion wires connect the vertical east and west sections of the primary gimbal to the wire supports which are connected across the annular groove of the gyro ball at the east and west sides (see figure 3.2).

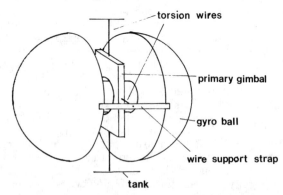

FIG. 3.2(a)   The gyro ball suspension showing torsion wires and primary gimbal.

Inspection of figure 3.2 should show that the gyro ball is free to tilt about the horizontal axis. This would twist the horizontal wires but the vertical wires would be unaffected as the primary gimbal will remain in the vertical plane. The gyro ball is also free to turn about the vertical axis, thus twisting the vertical wires without affecting the horizontal wires.

Power supplies are conducted to the gyro ball and the rotor through the torsion wires and through flexible silver conductors which are coiled around the torsion wires.

3.4   Purpose of the Torsion Wires

It must be stressed that the torsion wires do not support any of the weight of the gyro ball. This is done entirely by the liquid in which the ball is floating. The purpose of the torsion wires is to apply torques to the rotor, these torques arising from twists intentionally created in the wires. The vertical wires if twisted will apply a torque about the vertical axis, thereby causing a precession of the spin axis in tilt. A twist in the horizontal torsion wires will apply a torque about the horizontal axis and thereby cause a precession in azimuth. The twists in the wires may be created by causing the tank to rotate

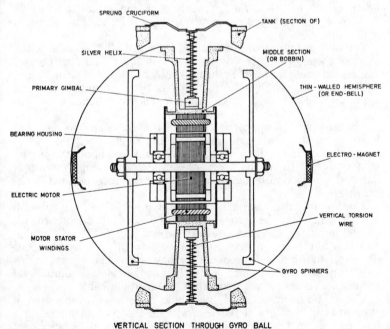

VERTICAL SECTION THROUGH GYRO BALL

Fig. 3.2(b)

about the appropriate axis with respect to the gyro ball. If the tank is made to turn in azimuth with respect to the ball then the vertical wires will twist. If the tank is made to rotate about the horizontal east–west axis, that is to tilt, with respect to the ball then the horizontal wires will twist. The control and the damping precessions, and also precessions to correct for errors are created in this way. Figure 3.2(b) shows a cross section through the gyro ball and primary gimbal and its connections to the tank.

3.5   The Tank and its Supporting Gimbals

The tank is a sealed container, the inside of which is spherical to conform to the spherical shape of the gyro ball. The clearance between the ball and the tank is filled with a liquid called fluorolube, the relative density of which is closely controlled to give the gyro ball the necessary neutral buoyancy. The earlier Arma Brown Mark 1C compass required a thermostatically controlled heater to maintain the fluorolube at an operating temperature of 85°C, in order to achieve the correct R.D. In this model the fluorolube solidified at lower temperatures to provide support to the gyro ball when the compass was stopped. Hi temp. and Lo temp. lights were included on the control panel to warn of incorrect operating temperatures. Later models (cold), use a fluorolube which maintains a constant R.D. over a wide range of temperature and no heating system is required.

The tank is mounted in a system of gimbals which minimise the effect of the ship's motion on the compass and which incorporates suspension axes about which the tank may be turned in azimuth and in tilt about the east–west horizontal axis, by an azimuth motor and a tilt motor respectively. This arrangement is shown schematically in figure 3.3.

The tank itself is supported within the tilt gimbal ring by means of bearings in the north–south axis of the tank. The tank hangs vertically within this tilt gimbal and any oscillation about the north–south axis, due to an east–west acceleration of the ship's motion, is damped out by viscous liquid damping devices incorporated in the bearings.

The horizontal tilt gimbal ring is supported within the azimuth gimbal, which is in the vertical east–west plane and supports the tilt gimbal in bearings in the east–west horizontal axis. The tilt gimbal and the tank therefore have the freedom to tilt, north end up or down, about this axis. Moreover they may be driven in tilt about this axis by the tilt motor which is attached to the azimuth gimbal and meshes with a gear segment attached to the tilt gimbal.

The azimuth gimbal, and the whole compass assembly that it supports can turn about the vertical axis, that is in azimuth, in a bearing mounted on the base plate of the compass, this component being rigidly attached to the ship. The azimuth motor which is

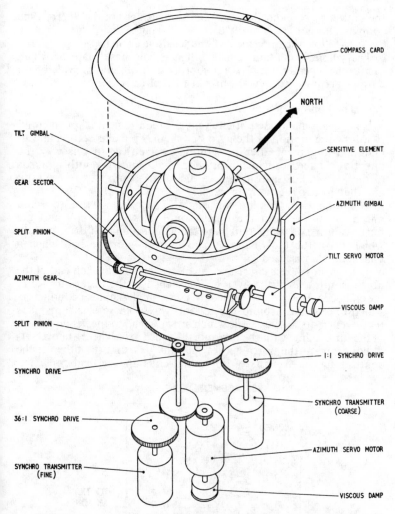

FIG. 3.3   Construction of the tank gimbals showing azimuth and tilt drives.

mounted on the base plate, meshes with the azimuth gear on the azimuth gimbal, and can drive the azimuth gimbal and therefore the tank in azimuth about the vertical axis.

The compass card is mounted on the top of the azimuth gimbal, the plane of which defines the east–west plane when the compass is settled. The north–south directions indicated on the compass card therefore coincide with the north–south axis of the tank. (Note that the tank may be likened to the phantom element of the Sperry type compass, in that it effectively carries the compass card, and must be made to follow the movement of the sensitive element.)

The whole is contained in a binnacle, the base plate of which carries the repeater transmission motors, and which is provided with a transparent top to view the master card directly.

3.6   The Follow Up System

It has been mentioned briefly that the requirement is for the tank to follow the motion of the gyro ball as the spin axis settles, and to maintain alignment after the compass is settled. In this way the directional reference which is provided by the north–south spin axis of the gyro ball is transmitted to the north–south axis of the tank and therefore to the compass card.

The follow up system consists of a sensing device to sense misalignment between the north–south axes of the ball and the north–south axis of the tank, and the azimuth and tilt drive motors which drive the tank back into alignment with the ball when a misalignment is sensed.

The sensing device consists of an electromagnet at each end of the north–south axis of the gyro ball, attached to the inside surface of the end bells. These are energised by a.c. through the silver conductors which are wound around the torsion wires. These electromagnets induce currents in sense coils which are attached to the inside surface of the tank in line with the tank north–south axis. There are two sets of coils, one at the north end of the tank axis and the other at the south. Each set consists of horizontal coils and vertical coils. The

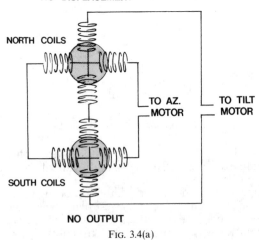

Fig. 3.4(a)

BODILY DISPLACEMENT

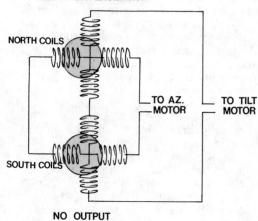

NO OUTPUT

FIG. 3.4(b)

ANGULAR DISPLACEMENT

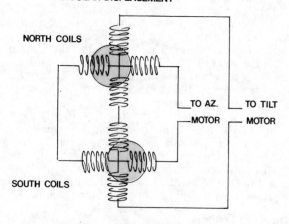

OUTPUT TO AZIMUTH MOTOR

FIG. 3.4(c)

theory of how these coils operate may be understood with reference
to figure 3.4. The north and south pairs of horizontal coils and
vertical coils are shown schematically with the electromagnets. The
north and south horizontal coils are wound in series, and similarly
the north and south vertical coils. When the north–south axis of the
gyro ball is correctly aligned with the north–south axis of the tank,

the electromagnets on the ball are symmetrical with the sense coils, as indicated in figure 3.4(a). Equal currents are then induced in the two sides of both north and south coils and the output is zero from both north and south coils. If a bodily displacement of the ball occurs relative to the tank, say the north–south ball axis moves to the west of the tank axis but remains parallel with it, an output results from the south horizontal coils as the electromagnet is not symmetrical with the south horizontal coils. An output also results from the north horizontal coils however and as they are in series, these two outputs are made to cancel. Similarly if a bodily displacement occurs vertically there will be no output from the vertical coils.

Consider however a displacement in azimuth between the ball axis and the tank axis, as shown in figure 3.4(c). There will be outputs from the north and the south horizontal coils, but they will now be of the same phase and will combine to give an output across the two horizontal coils. Similarly a tilt of the ball axis relative to the tank axis will produce an output from the vertical coils.

The purpose of the sense coils is therefore to sense an angular misalignment between the north–south axis of the tank and the ball, resolved into horizontal and vertical components, and to provide a.c. signals which are proportional to the misalignment. The output of the vertical sense coils is fed to the tilt motor after amplification. The tilt motor drives the tilt gimbal and tank in tilt in such a direction as to restore alignment with the gyro ball (see figure 3.3). The output of the horizontal coils, after amplification is fed to the azimuth motor, which drives the azimuth gimbal and therefore the tank in azimuth in such a direction as to restore alignment with the ball. The tank is therefore made to follow the movements of the ball, seeking a zero signal output from the sense coils.

The follow up is important in two respects. Firstly the follow up prevents any twists forming in the torsion wires as the gyro ball moves. This prevents the subsequent torques on the rotor, which would become cumulative as the torques cause more twists. Secondly the compass card north–south axis, as defined by the tank axis, is made to follow the spin axis, thus transmitting the directional reference provided by the spin axis to the compass card.

3.7   Control and Damping

The assembly described so far acts as a free gyro, the compass card registering the oscillations in azimuth of such a gyro. Nothing has been said about control or damping of the gyro. A control precession in azimuth, and a damping precession in tilt are created in order to cause the spin axis to seek and settle in the meridian. Both of these precessions must be proportional to the tilt. In the absence of a liquid gravity controlled ballistic there must be some other gravity sensing device to sense a tilt. This is provided by the pendulum unit which is attached to the top of the tank.

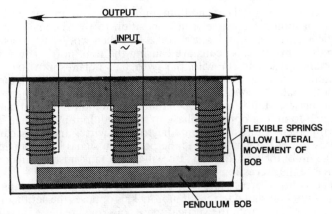

FIG. 3.5   The pendulum unit.

3.8   The Pendulum Unit

This gravity sensing device operates on the principle of the E-shaped transformer (figure 3.5). The primary of the transformer is wound on the central arm of the E, with two secondaries in series and wound in opposite directions, on the two outer arms of the E. The currents induced in the secondaries are controlled by the movement of an armature which moves as a pendulum, towards and away from the secondaries. (See section 2.8 for a more detailed explanation of the operation of the E-shaped transformer.) The movement of the pendulum armature is damped by immersion in a viscous silicone fluid so that short term accelerations due to the ship motions in a seaway are damped out and the pendulum only reacts to the long period tilt of the tank as it follows the gyro ball. The E-shaped core and the armature are aligned in the north–south axis so that only the north–south component of the tilt is sensed.

The output from the secondary windings of the pendulum unit is an a.c. voltage proportional to the tilt of the north–south axis of the tank, and of phase dependent upon the direction of the tilt. As in the operation of the gyro these tilts will be small, the operation is not affected by the fact that the movement of the pendulum armature is restricted to about $\frac{3}{4}°$. This means however that an output from the pendulum due to a north or south acceleration of the vessel, when altering course or speed, will be limited (see Ballistic Deflection).

3.9   The Use of the Pendulum Signal and the Follow Up Signals to Produce Control and Damping

The control precession and the damping precession may be considered together as they are both produced in the same manner. Both are proportional to the tilt. They are created by applying the

E

voltage output of the pendulum unit to the tilt motor and the azimuth motor respectively, in opposition to the signals from the vertical and horizontal sense coils. In other words, whereas the signals from the sense coils are causing the tank north–south axis to maintain alignment with the gyro ball north–south axis, the pendulum unit signal is used to drive the tank back out of alignment with the ball. An equilibrium will be reached, where a misalignment exists between tank and ball such that the resultant sense coil output is equal to and of opposite phase to the pendulum unit signal. This misalignment causes twists in the torsion wires, and thus causes precession of the gyro ball. As the pendulum signal is proportional to the tilt of the tank then so also will be the tank misalignment and therefore the precessions of the ball.

The control precession is produced by applying the amplified pendulum unit signal to the tilt motor. This opposes the action of the follow up signal from the vertical sense coils and creates a misalignment in tilt. The follow up system will cause the tank to maintain a misalignment where the pendulum signal is equal to the vertical sense coil signal. There will be a twist given to the horizontal torsion wires, which creates a torque on the ball about the horizontal east–west axis, and therefore a precession in azimuth, proportional to the tilt.

The damping precession is produced by applying the output of the pendulum unit, amplified to a voltage sufficient to give a torque $\frac{1}{33}$ of that of the control precession, to the azimuth motor. This opposes the action of the follow up signal from the horizontal sense coils and creates a misalignment in azimuth. The follow up system will cause the tank to maintain a misalignment where the pendulum unit signal is equal to the horizontal sense coil signal. There will be a twist of the vertical torsion wires, which creates a torque about the vertical axis, and therefore a precession in tilt, which will be proportional to the tilt.

Thus there will always be a slight misalignment between the tank and the gyro ball except when the tank axis is horizontal.

3.10   The Correction of Errors

The Arma Brown is corrected for latitude error and the course, latitude and speed error by feeding signals to the tilt and the azimuth motors in order to create additional misalignments between the tank and the ball, in the same manner as described for the control and damping of the compass. The resultant twists in the torsion wires provide precessions of the gyro ball to create a new equilibrium position in the meridian.

3.11   Correction of the Damping Error (Latitude Error)

The reason for the latitude error is stated fully in section 1.20. To summarise briefly, at the settling position the precessions and the movements of the spin axis due to the earth's rotation, must be in equilibrium. In all latitudes other than the equator the drift due to the earth's rotation will require an equal and opposite precession to compensate. Without correction the axis must settle with a tilt such that the control precession created will serve this purpose. The tilt however also provides some damping precession towards the horizon. The axis must therefore settle out of the meridian such that the tilting motion due to the earth's rotation acts away from the horizon to compensate for the damping precession. This deviation from the meridian is the damping or latitude error. In the Arma Brown however the effect of the drift due to the earth's rotation is compensated for by a correction precession in azimuth, derived from the error correction system. This precession is derived without any need for the axis to tilt so that with the axis horizontal when settled there is no damping precession in tilt and the axis must settle in the meridian, where tilting is zero.

A signal which is proportional to the drift is applied to the tilt motor to create a misalignment in tilt, a twist of the horizontal torsion wires and thus the required precession in azimuth. If the precession is to be equal to the drift then the precession must be proportional to the sine of the latitude (see Formula for Drift). It is therefore derived from a signal from the latitude potentiometer which must be correctly set by the navigator.

3.12 Correction of Course Latitude and Speed Error

In common with the Sperry Mark 20 compass this error is eliminated at source (see section 1.27). The spin axis is made to precess in tilt at a rate equal to the tilting introduced by the vessel's north–south velocity, that is at a rate of $v \cos$ course.

A signal which is derived from a cosine resolver and from a speed potentiometer gives a voltage which is proportional to $v \cos$ course. This is applied to the azimuth servo motor to create a misalignment in azimuth between the tank and the ball. The resultant twist of the vertical torsion wires precesses the spin axis in tilt at the required rate. The speed must be correctly set on the speed potentiometer by the navigator. The cosine function is provided by the windings of the synchro transmitter.

The synchro transmitter is part of the transmission system (see section 3.16). The stator windings of the 1 : 1 transmitter provide a signal proportional to the cosine of the course which is used for the steaming error correction. The output is presented across a variable resistor controlled by the speed setting (see figure 3.6).

As the course latitude and speed error is eliminated at source, the change in the value of the error does not cause the compass to require to resettle after an alteration of course or speed. The ballistic deflection is not therefore required to compensate for this, and the compass is not Schuler tuned. The ballistic deflection which remains

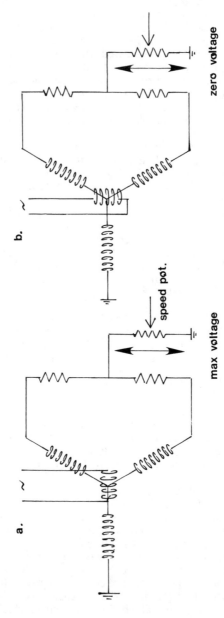

Fig 3.6   (a) Steaming error correction vessel heading north–south. (b) Steaming error correction vessel heading east–west.

as an unwanted effect is reduced by using a period of oscillation considerably longer than the Schuler period, and by limiting the movement of the pendulum unit which will sense the accelerations which cause the ballistic deflection. The viscosity of the fluid damping the pendulum will reduce the sensitivity of the unit to these accelerations.

3.13 The Arma Brown as a Directional Gyro

The Arma Brown is unique amongst marine gyro compasses in that it can be used as a directional gyro (see section 1.37). This facility has little application in merchant vessels which rarely go to such high latitudes as would necessitate use in this mode.

If the gyro is switched to 'free slew', the output of the pendulum unit is applied only to the azimuth servo motor. This eliminates the control precession, retaining only the damping precession towards the horizon. The precession towards the horizon will cause the gyro spin axis to level itself, without any tendency to seek the meridian. The axis will however drift in azimuth due to the earth's rotation at a rate of 15 sin lat. minutes of arc per minute of time.

However the latitude potentiometer setting causes a precession in azimuth equal and opposite to the drift when the latitude is set correctly (see section 3.11). This will eliminate the drift in azimuth of the self levelling gyro and the spin axis will therefore point to a constant direction without any north seeking property. It is therefore a directional gyro, and the direction in which the axis points may be set by means of the tilt and slew controls. The direction of the spin axis must be monitored at frequent intervals to retain a directional reference. The chosen direction should be fairly close to the meridian if not in the meridian itself, so that the tilting which will take the axis out of the horizontal, is small and will not gain a value greater than the damping precession which maintains the axis horizontal.

3.14 Transmission to Repeaters

Earlier marks of the Arma Brown compass used transmission by step by step motor to distant repeaters. The transmission system consisted of a rotary switch called a step by step motor, driven by the azimuth gear of the master compass, and a receiver motor to drive each repeater card, the motor receiver being driven by signals from the step by step motor. The electrical circuit for the transmission system is shown in figure 3.7.

The rotor of the transmitter is driven by direct gearing from the azimuth gear of the azimuth gimbal on the master compass. The azimuth drive motor turns the azimuth gear relative to the binnacle when the ship alters course as described in the 'follow up system'. The azimuth gear therefore automatically transmits this rotation through gearing to the rotor of the transmitter which is attached to

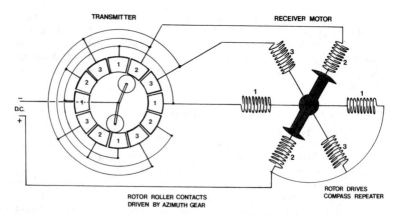

Fig. 3.7 Step by step transmission.

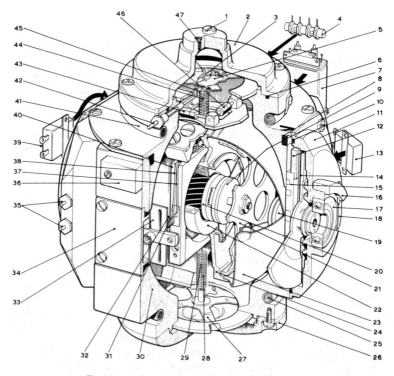

Fig. 3.8 The sensitive element of the Arma Brown.

the base of the binnacle. The rotary transmitter rotor carries two roller contacts at the extremities of the contact arms. As the rotor turns the roller contacts move across the inside surface of twelve segments which form a complete circle, the segments being insulated from each other, such that the roller contacts do not touch two segments at the same time. The segments are arranged in pairs, each contact in a pair opposite each other so that the two roller contacts normally only energise one pair of contacts which are connected together electrically. The roller contacts however are not diametrically opposed but are offset from this condition by 15°. The purpose of this offset is to provide an intermediate step where there are two pairs of segments energised as will be explained later.

Each pair of segments are connected in series with pairs of coils in the repeater motor. Only the pairs of coils which are connected to the segments which are contacted by the rollers in the transmitter can be energised. The whole therefore constitutes a multi contact rotary switch. As the rotor of the transmitter rotates, successive pairs of coils are energised, so that the magnetic field due to the current in the coils rotates in sympathy with the rotor of the transmitter. An armature suspended about an axis passing through the centre of the coils, rotates to line itself up with the magnetic field, and in so doing, through gearing turns the repeater compass card. Hence the rotation

---

Key to figure 3.8 — The sensitive element.
 1. Filler plug for fluorolube.
 2. Tank top cap.
 3. Flexible connection.
 4. Terminal strip for pendulum connection.
 5. Top cruciform.
 6. 'O' ring.
 7. Pendulum unit.
 8. 'O' ring.
 9. Motor bearing housing.
10. 'O' ring.
11. North bearing housing.
12. Pick up coil retaining plate.
13. Thermostatic switch (on hot compass).
14. Rotary damper disc.
15. Pick up coil.
16. Brush block.
17. North bearing.
18. Brush.
19. Electro magnet.
20. Electric motor (rotor).
21. Gyro wheel or spinner (northern one).
22. Motor (stator).
23. End bell.
24. Middle section or bobbin.
25. Calrod heater (on hot compass).
26. Tank bottom cap.
27. Bottom cruciform.
28. Bottom vertical helix.
29. Bottom vertical torsion wire.
30. Tank body.
31. East horizontal helix.
32. East horizontal torsion wire.
33. Torsion wire spring plate.
34. Side cover plate.
35. Pick up coil connections.
36. Balance weights.
37. Torsion wire electrical connection.
38. Helix strap electrical connection.
39. Thermostatic switch (on hot compass).
40. Primary gimbal.
41. Calrod heater (on hot compass).
42. Electrical connection to top cruciform.
43. Ball N/S balance nuts.
44. Top vertical torsion wire.
45. Top vertical helix.
46. Ball E/W balance nuts.
47. Breather.

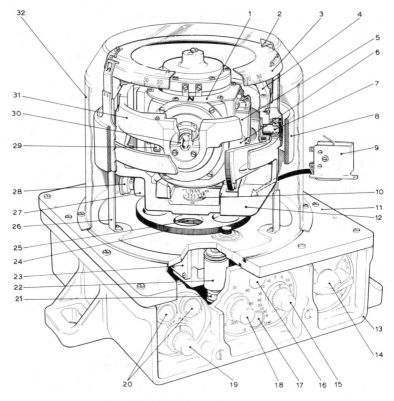

FIG. 3.9   Mark 1C Arma Brown compass.

Key to figure 3.9—General assembly of the Mark 1C compass.

1. Tank assembly (Sensitive element).
2. Lubber line.
3. Compass card.
4. Spirit level bracket.
5. Pendulum unit.
6. Thermostatic switch (on hot compass).
7. West tilt trunnion.
8. Binnacle heater (on hot compass).
9. Thermostatic switch (on hot compass).
10. Shaft terminal pins.
11. Azimuth drive plate.
12. Secondary azimuth gimbal.
13. Control box.
14. Selector switch.
15. Latitude control.
16 and 17. Hi and Low temp. lights (on hot compass).

18. Speed control.
19. Slew rate control.
20. Slew push buttons to actuate slew controls.
21. Viscous damp (azimuth).
22. Azimuth servo motor.
23. Slip ring brush block.
24. Azimuth gear.
25. Fine synchro drive gear.
26. Lubber line support bracket.
27. Tilt servo motor.
28. Viscous damp (tilt).
29. Tilt limit shock absorber.
30. North trunnion.
31. Secondary tilt gimbal.
32. Binnacle casing.

of the azimuth gear with the master card attached is transmitted to the repeater cards.

The offset of the two roller contacts on the contact arm of the transmitter rotor provides intermediate steps in the sequence of energising the coils. Without this offset the sequence as the rotor turns would be pair 1, pair 2, pair 3, pair 1, etc. Due to the offset however there is a stage where one roller contact energises a different pair to the opposite roller contact, as indicated in figure 3.6. The sequence will therefore be pair 1, pairs 1 and 2, pair 2, pairs 2 and 3, pair 3, pairs 3 and 1, pair 1, etc. When two pairs of coils are energised the resultant magnetic field will lie between the pairs of coils and the receiver armature will line itself up accordingly. This intermediate step provides for smoother operation.

The transmitter rotor turns through a cycle of six positions on the commutator segments for each degree turned by the master compass. As there are twenty-four steps in a complete rotation of the rotor, the master compass must turn through $4°$ to achieve this. The rotor of the receiver turns twice for each revolution of the rotor of the transmitter, so that each time the receiver armature rotor turns through $360°$ the repeater card must turn through $2°$. The gearing of the repeater card to the repeater motor armature has therefore a gearing ratio of $180 : 1$.

3.15   The Relay Transmitter

In practice the rotary transmitter on the master compass operates a relay transmitter located in the junction box. The relay transmitter, of similar design and operation to the rotary transmitter described then operates the repeaters and ancillaries such as gyro stabilisation and auto pilot. If the number of repeaters and ancillaries are too great however, and present too great an electrical load, the relay transmitter drives a second relay transmitter, and the load is shared between the two.

3.16   Synchro Transmission

Later marks of the Arma Brown incorporate a synchro transmission system using two synchro transmitters which are driven through gearing from the master compass azimuth gear. One transmitter has a $1 : 1$ gear ratio and the other a $36 : 1$ ratio. The $1 : 1$ transmitter may be used for transmission to radar and D/F stabilisation inputs where there is no mechanical load on the receiver. The higher geared transmitter is used to serve compass repeaters, the high gearing giving smoother and more sensitive operation and less load on the receiver motor. The $1 : 1$ transmitter also provides a cosine function for steaming error correction.

CHAPTER 4

THE ANSCHÜTZ GYRO COMPASS

4.1 Introduction

This chapter describes three of the Anschütz compasses in current use. The basic Anschütz design is described in detail for the Standards 3 and 4 which are identical compasses apart from the provision of transmission to repeaters in the Standard 4. This design has changed little in the history of the Anschütz compass, apart from the modern tendency towards smaller compact compasses, a trend which is evident in the latest Anschütz compasses, the Standards 6 and 10 being described here. The main features of the successful design however are retained in these compasses and much that is common to the Standards 4, 6, and 10 is omitted having been dealt with for the Standard 4. The description of the Standard 4 should be understood first therefore.

4.2 Construction of the Anschütz Standards 3 and 4

The Sensitive Element

The sensitive element of the Anschütz design consists of the gyrosphere which contains two coupled gyros rotating at 20 000 r.p.m. Each gyro has freedom to rotate in azimuth only, being supported in bearings in a vertical axis within the gyrosphere. One gyro spin axis points approximately north-east and the other approximately north-west. Although the gyros have only two degrees of freedom the gyrosphere itself has freedom to tilt as its suspension is by immersion in an electrolytic liquid within an outer sphere. The electrolyte is distilled water with added glycerine and benzoic acid. This is used to conduct power supplies to the gyrosphere.

The Outer Sphere

The gyrosphere is supported within the outer sphere with very small clearance between the two (from 4 to 6 mm). The gyrosphere is immersed in the electrically conductive liquid with a small negative buoyancy so that with the compass stopped it rests on the bottom of the outer sphere. When the compass is running the gyrosphere is maintained centrally within the outer sphere by the action of a repulsion coil which is fitted horizontally around the lower section of the gyrosphere. This coil is fed with one phase of the gyrosphere supply which induces current in the lower section of the outer sphere. Interaction of magnetic fields produces a repelling

118

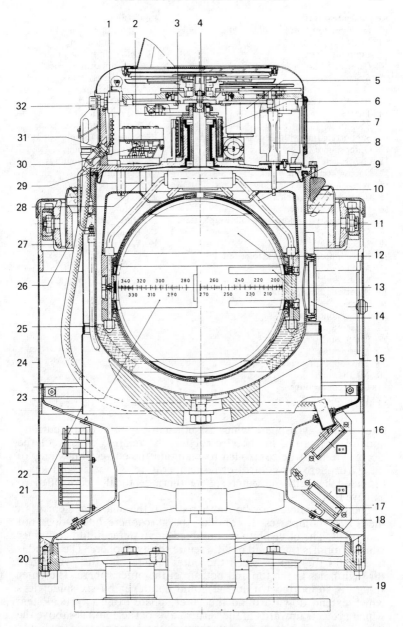

FIG. 4.1(a) Sectional diagram Anschütz Standard 4 compass.

Key to figure 4.1(a).
1. Dimming resistance for illumination.
2. Clip on engaging arm.
3. Coupling block.
4. Centring ball of gear plate.
5. Azimuth motor.
6. Slip ring assembly.
7. Inspection window for temperature readings.
8. Thermometer.
9. Spider leg.
10. Supporting ring with suspension springs.
11. Outer sphere.
12. Gyrosphere.
13. Narrow conducting band.
14. Window of liquid container.
15. Compensating weight.
16. Follow up amplifier.
17. Symmetrical transformer of follow up system.
18. Motor with fan.
19. Shock mounts.
20. Bolt connecting binnacle to pedestal.
21. Air duct.
22. Rubber skirt.
23. Broad conducting band.
24. Binnacle.
25. Liquid container.
26. Inner gimbal ring.
27. Outer gimbal ring.
28. Thermostat.
29. Top supporting plate.
30. Microswitch.
31. Cable connections.
32. Dimmer knob.

Key to figure 4.1(b).
1. Liquid container.
2. Inner gimbal ring.
3. Outer gimbal ring.
4. Top supporting plate.
5. Slip ring assembly.
6. Azimuth gear.
7. Compass card.
8. Azimuth motor.
9. Vertical stem bearings.
10. Spider leg assembly.
11. Annular damping vessel.
12. Rotor stator windings.
13. East rotor.
14. Gyrosphere.
15. Repulsion coils.
16. Rotor vertical axis bearings.
17. Outer sphere.
18. Electrolytic liquid.
19. West rotor casing.

force on the gyrosphere which is sufficient to maintain it centrally and freely floating in the electrolyte. The relative density of the electrolyte must be controlled to maintain the correct buoyancy of the gyrosphere, by control of its temperature. A heater and fan is provided beneath the outer sphere thermostatically controlled to achieve this.

The outer sphere may be compared with the phantom element of the Sperry compasses. It contains the gyrosphere but it does not support it. The electrolyte is contained in an outer liquid container which supports the liquid and therefore the gyrosphere. The liquid is free to fill the gap between the outer sphere and the gyrosphere through holes in the top and bottom of the outer sphere. The outer sphere is supported within the liquid container by six spider legs which extend down around the outer sphere from a vertical stem which projects upwards in the vertical axis of the compass above the outer sphere. This stem projects through the cover plate of the liquid

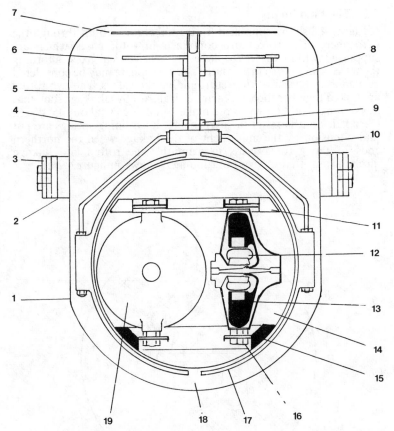

FIG. 4.1(b) Simplified diagram of main components of Anschütz Standards 3 and 4.

container supported by bearings in the vertical axis. Above the liquid container the vertical stem carries a slip ring assembly, the azimuth gear, and the compass card. The liquid container, which is equivalent to the stationary element is attached to the vessel supported within the binnacle via the inner and outer gimbal rings which contain pivots to allow the compass to hang vertically against the motion of the vessel.

When the vessel alters course the binnacle and outer liquid container remain aligned with the ship. The outer sphere, spider legs and compass card (phantom element), are turned within the outer container by the azimuth motor, through the azimuth gear, in order to remain aligned with the sensitive element. This is achieved by the follow up system.

4.3   The Twin Rotors

Figure 4.2 shows simplified horizontal cross sections through the gyrosphere. The rotors are contained in rotor cases which are supported within the gyrosphere in their vertical axes, affording them freedom to turn in azimuth. The gyrosphere may be considered as a spherical 'vertical ring' surrounding the rotors. The two rotors are linked together through their vertical axes by a linkage such that the spin axes of the two rotors make equal angles (about 45°), with the north–south axis of the gyrosphere. Restraining springs are put under tension by the movement of the linkage when the northern ends of the gyros precess in azimuth. The rotors and linkage mechanism with the gyros not running is shown in figure 4.2(a).

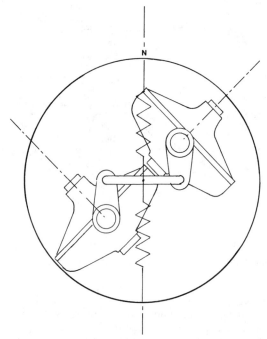

Fig. 4.2(a)   The gyrosphere. Rotors not running.

The rotors spin by induction at 20 000 r.p.m. clockwise as viewed from the south, that is the direction associated with a bottom heavy gyro. Both gyros have components of angular momentum in the north–south plane which combine to provide the north seeking property when suitably controlled. When the gyros are running and the compass settled, the rotors are subject to a precession of their northern ends towards the meridian due to their confinement in their vertical axes. The north end of the axis of the east rotor will experience upwards tilting as it is directed to the east of the meridian, but the restraining force of the vertical axis bearings puts a torque on the rotor about the horizontal axis which causes the north-east end to precess towards the meridian. Similarly the west rotor, being directed to the west of the meridian experiences a downwards tilting of the northern end which will cause that end to precess to the east, again towards the meridian. These precessions, through the linkage, tension the springs as shown in figure 4.2(b). This tension causes a torque about the vertical axes, clockwise as viewed from above on the east rotor and anticlockwise on the west rotor. These torques about the vertical axes cause precessions in tilt about the horizontal

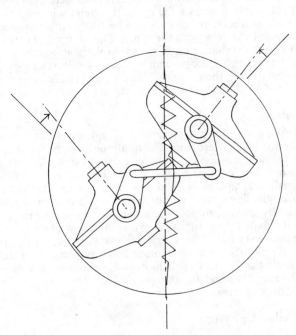

FIG. 4.2(b) Rotors running.

axes which oppose the tilting due the earth's rotation in each case, so that there is an equilibrium with the northern ends precessed slightly towards the meridian with the springs under tension. The angle through which the axes precess will be determined by the rate of tilting which depends upon the latitude.

The north–south axis of the gyrosphere will seek and settle in the meridian, when suitably controlled and damped, as when this axis is to the east of the meridian the upwards tilting of the north end of the east rotor will be greater than the downwards tilting of the north end of the west rotor (tilt varies as the sine of the azimuth). The gyrosphere will therefore tilt upwards and the action of the control element will precess the gyrosphere to the west to initiate the usual settling spiral.

4.4   Control of the Anschütz

Control of the compass is achieved by making the gyrosphere bottom heavy, the centre of gravity being secured below the centre of buoyancy. When the gyrosphere tilts the upwards force of buoyancy and the downwards force of the weight are no longer in the same vertical line and a righting couple is produced. This bottom heavy control couple precesses the gyros through their vertical axis bearings, both in the same direction. The rotors are required to rotate clockwise as viewed from the south. This method of control is possible due to the stabilisation of the gyrosphere about the north–south axis by the twin rotors, which prevents rolling errors. The period of oscillation in the north seeking ellipse is the Schuler period for a latitude of 54°.

4.5   Damping

The compass is damped by a precession in azimuth (see section 1.21, Damping towards the Meridian). The damping element is contained in the gyrosphere consisting of a circular trough divided into compartments. The compartments are connected in north–south pairs by small bore apertures. When the gyrosphere tilts, oil in the damping troughs flows between north and south compartments to the low side, by gravity, to produce a top heavy type torque about the horizontal axis. The constriction of the interconnecting apertures causes the necessary lag in the maximum displacement of liquid, so that the resulting precession in azimuth is out of phase with the tilt which causes it. Section 1.21 explains how this produces a precession towards the meridian and the damping effect. The compass is not subject to damping error.

4.6   The Follow Up System

The north–south axis of the compass card which is carried on the vertical stem of the spider legs and outer sphere assembly, must be maintained in alignment with the north–south axis of the gyrosphere. The outer sphere is made to follow up the gyrosphere by the follow up system.

The outer sphere is driven by the azimuth motor through the azimuth gear. The azimuth motor is carried on the top plate of the liquid container which remains stationary relative to the ship, and which carries the vertical stem bearings. A signal which is proportional to the misalignment of the outer sphere and the gyrosphere is obtained from a wheatstone bridge sensing element.

The gyrosphere carries a horizontal semicircular band of graphite ebonite conducting surface around its centre. This conductive band is part of the electrical supply to the gyrosphere (see section 4.7), and carries one phase of the three phase supply but also energises the wheatstone bridge circuit. When the outer sphere and the gyrosphere are correctly aligned this semicircular band is symmetrical with two diametrically opposed electrical contacts on the inside of the outer sphere. Electrical contact is made between the conductive band and the contacts by the electrolyte in which the gyrosphere is immersed. Under conditions of correct alignment the two electrolytic paths are equal and the wheatstone bridge is balanced. The two outer sphere contacts will be at the same potential and the error signal taken from these contacts will be zero. If the gyrosphere rotates within the outer sphere the electrolytic paths are no longer the same length and the voltage drop across them will not be the same. The two contacts will not be at the same potential and an error signal will be obtained. This output will be of phase dependent upon the direction of misalignment and of magnitude proportional to the displacement. After amplification the output signal drives the azimuth motor which turns the outer sphere to restore alignment with the gyrosphere and zero error signal. Figure 4.3 shows the arrangement of the conductive band and follow up contacts and the equivalent electrical network.

The supply to the conductive band on the gyrosphere is through

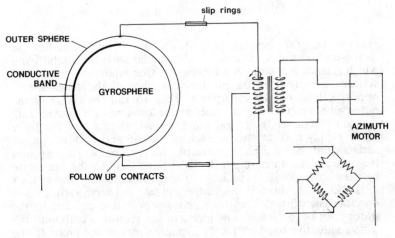

FIG. 4.3 Follow up system.

the electrolyte. The error signal from the outer sphere follow up contacts is taken to the azimuth motor via the spider legs and slip ring assembly.

4.7   Electrical Supply to the Gyrosphere

The rotors are energised with a three phase supply, one phase of which is used to energise the follow up system and one phase to energise the repulsion coils.

Supply is taken to the slip ring assembly around the vertical stem of the spider leg assembly. The supply is then carried down through the spider legs and onto the outer sphere. Current flows from the outer sphere to the gyrosphere via the electrolyte which surrounds the gyrosphere and separates it from the outer sphere. For this

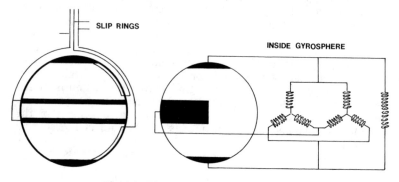

Fig. 4.4   Electrical supply to the gyrosphere.

purpose the gyrosphere has graphite ebonite conductive surfaces at its top and bottom extremities, and a similar wide horizontal band which extends half way round its centre. Corresponding conductive surfaces are provided on the inside surface of the outer sphere opposite those on the gyrosphere. That around the centre of the outer sphere consists of an upper and a lower narrow contact ring extending completely around the sphere. One phase of the three phase supply is connected to each of the top and bottom contact surfaces and the third phase to the two narrow contact rings around the centre of the outer sphere. Current flows through the electrolyte between corresponding surfaces to the gyrosphere via paths of least resistance, and there is negligible current between surfaces not opposite each other. The three phase supply is connected to the stator coils of the rotors, one phase to the repulsion coils, and the wide conductive band on the gyrosphere supplies one phase to the follow up system as described in section 4.6.

4.8 Error Correction

The Anschütz compass, being damped in azimuth, is not subject to damping error. The course latitude and speed error (steaming error), is not corrected but must be extracted from tables and applied as a compass error. The change in the value of the course latitude and speed error due to an alteration of course or speed is compensated for by the ballistic deflection by adopting the Schuler period for a latitude of 54°. Small errors may be introduced in other latitudes after alterations of course or speed while the compass resettles, but their magnitude will be small.

4.9 Elimination of Rolling Error

The first rolling error is eliminated by careful design of the gyrosphere. The distribution of mass is such that the moments on inertia of the cross section is equalised in all vertical planes (see section 1.29).

The second rolling error is eliminated by the two gyro configuration which provides stabilisation about the north–south axis. The components of angular momentum in the east–west plane prevent oscillation of the gyrosphere in that plane. This maintains the centre of gravity of the gyrosphere in the north–south plane thus preventing rolling errors (see section 1.31). It was explained in section 4.3 that with the gyros running and the compass settled the northern ends of the two rotors are precessed slightly towards the meridian, a condition which creates a balance between the tilting due to the earth's rotation and the tilting due to the tension in the springs of the rotor linkage when the rotors precess in azimuth. If the gyrosphere attempts to tilt about its north–south axis, then as the rotors possess inertia in the east–west plane this represents a tilting of the rotors with respect to the gyrosphere, which effectively increases or decreases the tilting being experienced by the rotors due to the earth's rotation. This upsets the balance between this tilting and the precessions in tilt caused by the tension in the linkage springs, and the rotors precess in azimuth to retension the springs to restore the equilibrium. The rate of precession is low due to the high inertia of the rotors and the angle through which the rotors precess during a half roll period is small. The opposite side of the roll will produce a precession in the reverse direction so that the rotors have a slight nodding of their axes towards and away from the meridian when the vessel is rolling. The rotors precess by equal amounts, maintaining the equality of the angles between the rotor axes and the meridian.

4.10 The Anschütz Standard 6

The Standard 6 compass is a small compact compass, which while retaining the basic principles of the Anschütz design described for the Standard 4, incorporates modifications to the suspension of the

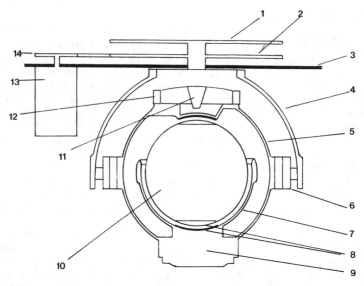

FIG. 4.5   Simplified sectional view showing main components of the Standard 6 compass.

Key to figure 4.5.
 1. Compass card.
 2. Azimuth gear.
 3. Top supporting plate.
 4. Vertical gimbal.
 5. Outer sphere.
 6. Horizontal gimbal.
 7. Inner hemisphere.
 8. Conducting dome and surface.
 9. Pump unit.
10. Gyrosphere.
11. Plexiglass inspection cone.
12. Damping vessel.
13. Azimuth motor.
14. Gearing.

sensitive element which simplify the construction and reduce the overall size. The outer sphere is a sealed container, obviating the need for an outer liquid container, and houses a hydraulic pump which replaces the repulsion coils in the support of the gyrosphere in the electrolyte. The spider leg assembly is redesigned and incorporates a gimbal system, such a system no longer being required around the binnacle or casing. The casing is supported directly on the vessel through shock proof mountings. The main constituent parts of the Standard 6 are illustrated in the simplified cross section shown in figure 4.5.

4.11   The Gyrosphere

The sensitive element of the compass is the gyrosphere which is of the same basic design as that described for the Standard 4, but is less than half the size being only about $11\frac{1}{2}$ cm in diameter. It contains twin rotors in a helium atmosphere, rotating at 12 000 r.p.m. The sphere is controlled by making its centre of gravity below its centre of buoyancy and damped in azimuth by an annular damping vessel. It is tuned to the Schuler period. The shell of the gyrosphere carries conductive domes at its top and bottom which receive one phase each of the three phase supply required for the rotors. The third phase is produced by adjusting one of these phases by capacitors. A semicircular conducting band around the centre of the gyrosphere is provided as part of the follow up system.

4.12 The Outer Sphere

The outer sphere is the phantom or follow up element which carries the compass card. Unlike the Standard 4 this is a sealed spherical shell and supports the electrolyte in which the sensitive element is floated. This allows the outer liquid container of the Standard 4 to be dispensed with. The outer sphere is made up of the upper hemispherical shell, an equatorial ring, and a lower hemispherical shell. This latter part contains an inner hemisphere in which the gyrosphere is located with a small clearance. The small negative buoyancy of the gyrosphere is overcome by a centrifugal pump unit in the bottom of the outer sphere which delivers a flow of electrolyte upwards and around the gyrosphere in the small clearance between it and the inner hemisphere. This maintains the gyrosphere floating freely and centrally in the outer sphere and provides a virtually friction free suspension for the sensitive element.

Conductive domes at the top and bottom of the outer sphere correspond to those on the gyrosphere. The top of the outer sphere incorporates an inspection cover with a filler plug and a visible means of checking the level of the electrolyte in the outer sphere.

4.13 The Gimbal Support

The outer sphere is supported by a gimbal support which replaces the spider leg assembly of the Standard 4. The sphere is carried within a horizontal ring supported by horizontal bearings in the north–south axis, while this ring is supported through horizontal bearings in the east–west axis by a vertical half ring which extends upwards to a vertical stem the top of which carries the compass card. The compass assembly is supported by bearings around the vertical stem carried by the top supporting plate, which is the top cover of the compass casing. The compass assembly may be rotated in these bearings relative to the supporting plate by the azimuth servo motor in order to maintain alignment of the outer sphere with the gyrosphere when the vessel alters course. The azimuth motor is carried on the top supporting plate as is the transmitter of the repeater system.

4.14   The Compass Casing

The compass casing of which the top supporting plate forms the top cover, encloses the compass assembly, which is supported from the top plate. The compass unit hangs vertically into but without contact with, a screening case attached to the bottom of the casing. This screening case contains six heating lamps which, together with a cooling fan maintains an operating temperature of $52° \pm 10\%$, controlled thermostatically by microswitches in the outer sphere. Also contained in the casing is the transformer of the follow up system and amplifier panels.

For access to the compass assembly for maintenance, the supporting plate hinges upwards bringing the compass assembly with it. The compass must hang vertically in its gimbals however and to achieve this the follow up system must be switched off. The azimuth motor is then controlled by a push button on the inside wall of the casing. This turns the gimbals until the bearings between the horizontal gimbal ring and the outer gimbal ring are horizontal allowing the compass to hang horizontally. The supporting plate may then be hinged back vertically which provides access to the top of the outer sphere. This will be necessary to check and top up the electrolyte in the outer sphere with distilled water.

4.15   Anschütz Standard 10

The Standard 10 is a small compact steering compass of basic design comparable to the Standard 6 but simplified by the omission of any follow up arrangement. Instead the directional reference is taken directly from the sensitive element which is visible through transparent outer components of the gyro compass. A graduated scale of degrees is provided around the circumference of the gyrosphere for this purpose. The outer sphere described for the Standard 6 becomes part of the stationary element which remains aligned with the vessel during an alteration of course, and carries the lubber line in the fore and aft line.

The implications of such a uniquely simplified design are such that the Standard 10 is essentially a small ship or yacht compass. The absence of any follow up motion means that there is no drive to repeater systems available. The main components of the Standard 10 are shown in the simplified cross section in figure 4.6.

4.16   Construction of the Standard 10

A gyrosphere of the usual Anschütz design as described for the Standards 4 and 6 comprises the sensitive element of the compass. A scale of degrees is engraved around the circumference slightly above its equator, and this scale is visible and serves as a compass card. The gyrosphere is supported within an outer sphere which is made up of an upper hemisphere and a lower hemisphere joined and sealed

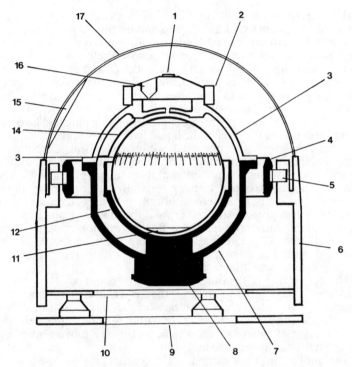

FIG 4.6   Simplified sectional view of Standard 10 gyro compass.

Key to figure 4.6.
1. Electrolyte filler plug.
2. Damping vessel.
3. Transparent upper hemisphere of outer sphere.
4. Gimbal ring.
5. Gimbal bearing.
6. Casing.
7. Lower hemisphere of outer sphere.
8. Pump unit.
9. Base plate.
10. Adjustable connecting plate.
11. Conducting surface.
12. Inner hemisphere.
13. Gyrosphere and graduated scale.
14. Lubber line.
15. Magnifying lens.
16. Electrolyte level inspection cone.
17. Transparent dome.

around its equator. The upper hemisphere is transparent allowing direct viewing of the gyrosphere with its scale. A lubber line is carried on the inside of the outer sphere against which the gyrosphere scale is viewed. The lower hemisphere contains an inner hemisphere in which the gyrosphere is located. Its slight negative buoyancy will cause the gyrosphere to rest on the bottom of the inner hemisphere when the compass is stopped, the outer sphere being filled with a liquid consisting of distilled water and glycerine with an additive to make it electrically conductive. Electrical supply to the gyrosphere is achieved by conductive domes at top and bottom of the gyrosphere and outer spheres as in the Standard 6. A centrifugal pump unit in the base of the outer sphere supplies a flow of electrolyte upwards and around the gyrosphere into the small clearance between the gyrosphere and the inner hemisphere, and this maintains the gyrosphere freely floating and centralised, providing a virtually friction free suspension for the sensitive element.

The top of the outer sphere incorporates a filling plug and a visible means of checking the level of the liquid in the outer sphere.

The outer sphere is supported within the casing or binnacle in gimbal mountings consisting of an inner and an outer horizontal gimbal ring with bearings between them in perpendicular axes, allowing the compass unit to hang vertically against ship motions. Movement of the outer sphere within the gimbals is damped by an annular damping vessel situated around the top of the outer sphere. This contains liquid, the restricted flow of which passively damps any oscillations in the gimbals. This damping vessel should not be confused with the damping arrangement within the gyrosphere which produces a north reference.

The connection of the outer sphere to the casing via the gimbals fixes the outer sphere relative to the vessel, and the lubber line attached to the outer sphere must be adjusted to the fore and aft line of the ship. The gyrosphere will turn within the outer sphere during an alteration of course which is indicated by the movement of the gyrosphere scale against the lubber line.

The gimbal rings are carried in the compass casing which has a transparent top hemispherical dome through which the compass is viewed. A magnifying lens is incorporated opposite the lubber line for ease of viewing. The lower binnacle contains a thermostatically controlled fan which switches on and off at 35°C. Additional heating may be provided for operation in low temperatures. The casing is attached to the vessel via base plates which allow adjustment of the compass to the vessel's fore and aft line.

The compass unit requires a static inverter unit which converts ship's mains to the 55 volt 400 Hz supply for the rotors and the 11 volt d.c. supply for the cooling fan.

APPENDIX

Alternating Current

In an alternating current the direction and magnitude of the current flow are changing sinusoidally. A sine wave graph may be used to show the variation in current flow with time, or to show the variation in voltage across a resistance with time. In a purely resistive circuit (no value of inductance or capacitance), the voltage and current sine waves are in phase with each other. (The maximums occur at the same time and the zero values occur at the same time etc.)

Figure A.1 shows current and voltage waveforms. The horizontal

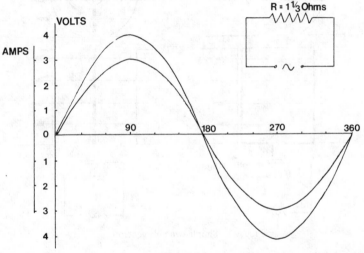

FIG. A.1

axis is the time axis but may also be expressed in degrees, 0°–360° representing one complete cycle of the sine wave. This notation will repeat itself after each cycle.

The maximum value that the voltage or current attains is called the Peak Voltage.

The number of cycles of 360° through which the value changes in one second is called the frequency of the supply. Frequency is measured in cycles per second of which the S.I. unit is the Hertz (Hz). 1 Hz = 1 c/s.

Electromagnetic Induction

If a straight conductor cuts through or is cut by lines of magnetic force an e.m.f. is generated in the conductor which is proportional to the rate of cutting. An alternating current may be generated by rotating a conductor in the form of a loop in a magnetic field. Figure A.2 shows such a conductor. An e.m.f. is generated in the two parallel arms of the loop when they are moving perpendicularly to the direction of the field. The maximum e.m.f. will therefore be generated with the loop in the position shown in figure A.2(a). With the loop rotated through 90° to the position shown in figure A.2(b)

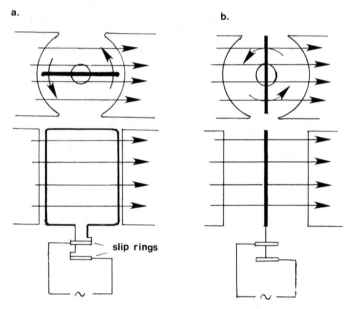

FIG. A.2   Simple two pole generator.

the conductors are moving along the direction of the field and there is no e.m.f. generated. If the loop now rotates a further 90° the e.m.f. will again be maximum but of opposite polarity. If the ends of the loop are connected across a load resistance via slip rings as shown in figure A.2 an alternating voltage will be generated across R and alternating current will flow.

The frequency of the a.c. will depend upon the speed at which the loop is rotated. One cycle of a.c. will be produced for each revolution of the loop, which in a practical generator will consist of multiple windings, if there is one pair of poles used as illustrated. The frequency may be increased without increasing the driving speed by using more than one pair of poles. The frequency will be the product of the number of pairs of poles and the number of revolutions per second.

Multi Phase Supplies

Two and three phase supplies are used widely for driving motors. The rotor of a gyro is driven from a three phase supply while a two phase supply is used for servo motors.

A two phase supply consists of two separate alternating voltages of equal amplitude but displaced in phase by 90°. (The maximum of one voltage lags the maximum of the other by one quarter of a cycle.) A two phase supply is shown in figure A.4. A two phase supply may be generated by using two separate windings on the simple two pole generator shown in figure A.2, with the planes of the windings at right angles. The angle between the planes of the windings will determine the phase difference between the two phases.

A three phase supply may be generated by using three separate windings with their planes at 120° intervals. The three phases will be taken off via three sets of slip rings. An important property of such a three phase supply is that the algebraic sum of the values of the three phases at any instant in time is zero. This may be verified by inspection of figure A.5 which shows the three phase supply.

Power supplies to a gyro compass are normally derived from a three phase generator driven by a motor from the ship's mains supply.

Induction Motors

Induction motors are widely used in gyro technology for driving the rotor and for servo motors for azimuth follow up and for error correction. Driving a rotor by induction depends upon the production of a rotating magnetic field by supplying the different phases of a multiphase supply to separate windings on a stator core. A rotating field may be produced by any number of phases of two or more. Servo motors are usually of two phase design while rotors are normally driven by a three phase supply.

Rotating Field by Two Phase Supply

Consider figure A.3 which shows two windings on a core, mutually at right angles. Winding A is fed with the current of phase A in figure A.4 and coil B is fed with the current of phase B which is 90° lagging the phase of A. At time x when phase A supply is maximum positive and phase B supply is zero there will be current flowing in the A windings as indicated in figure A.3(a). The field will be as shown with its axis perpendicular to the plane of the A windings. There is at this instant no current and therefore no field associated with the B windings. One eighth of a cycle (45°) later, at time y

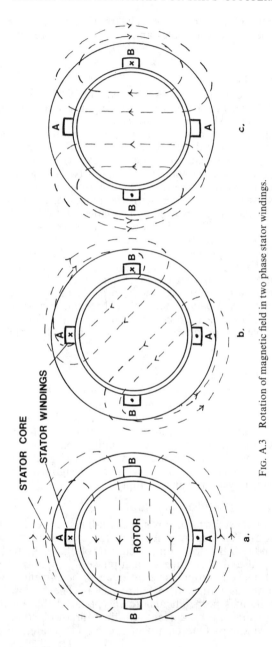

Fig. A.3 Rotation of magnetic field in two phase stator windings.

in figure A.4 the two phases both have values of 0·7071 of the maximum value, currents are flowing in both windings as indicated in figure A.3(b) and the axis of the resultant magnetic field will lie as shown having turned through 45° to a direction between those of the planes of the two windings. One eighth of a cycle (45°) later, at time z in figure A.4 phase B current is maximum and phase A zero. The B windings will have current as indicated in figure A.3(c) and the magnetic field will be that associated with the B windings only as shown. The axis of the field has turned through a further 45°.

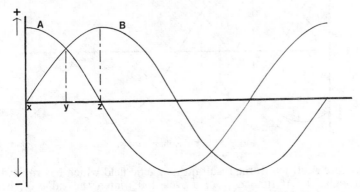

FIG. A.4   A two phase supply.

The direction of the rotation of the magnetic field may be reversed by reversing the connections of one of the supply phases, so that the lagging phase becomes the leading phase and vice versa. This is important in gyro servo motors which usually are required to be phase conscious, that is to rotate in a direction which depends upon the phase of the control signal. For example, the azimuth motor of the gyro follow up system must turn in such a direction as to realign the phantom ring with the sensitive element. Its control signal is derived from a device which senses the misalignment between phantom and sensitive element and provides an a.c. signal the phase of which depends upon the direction of the misalignment. The appropriate direction of rotation of the motor is produced by feeding a signal of constant phase to the reference coil of the two phase motor. The control signal will therefore lead or lag the reference phase by 90° depending upon the direction of the misalignment.

Rotation of a Magnetic Field by Three Phase Supply

Figure A.5 shows a three phase supply, and figure A.6 three stator windings on a core, each winding displaced 120° from the others. Figure A.6(a) shows the current flow in the windings and the resultant magnetic field for a time x when the A phase is maximum positive and the value of phases B and C is 0·5 the maximum value negative. At some time $\frac{1}{12}$ of a cycle (30°) later the A phase has a value of 0·866 max., the B phase is zero value, and the C phase is 0·866 negative. The current flow in the A, B and C windings is shown

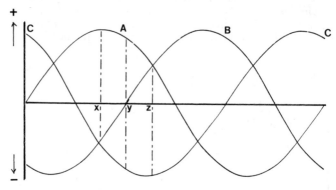

Fig. A.5   A three phase supply.

in figure A.6(b) with the resultant magnetic field which has rotated through 30°. At time z, $\frac{1}{12}$ of a cycle (30°) later, the value of the A phase is 0·5 max., the value of the B phase is the same and the value of the C phase is maximum negative. Figure A.6(c) shows the current flow in the A, B and C windings and the resultant magnetic field which has rotated through a further 30°. The direction of rotation may be reversed by reversing any two of the three stator connections.

The rotor of an induction motor consists of a core which carries conductors which are cut by the rotating magnetic flux produced by the stator windings. The conductors may consist of copper bars which are connected at each end to form a 'squirrel cage' formation. The cutting of the conductors of the rotor by the rotating magnetic flux induces currents in them, the magnetic field of which interacts with the rotating field and produces a force on the conductors which exerts a torque on the rotor in the direction of the rotating field of the stator. The production of this torque is the same principle as that of the electric motor. The rotor will rotate at some speed which is less than the speed of rotation of the stator field. If the rotor achieved the same speed as the stator field, then there would be no cutting of rotor conductors by the stator field. The greater the speed of rotation of the stator field relative to the rotor conductors then the greater will be the torque exerted on the rotor. The rotor will rotate at some speed below that of the stator field such that the torque developed on the rotor is sufficient to overcome the load on the rotor.

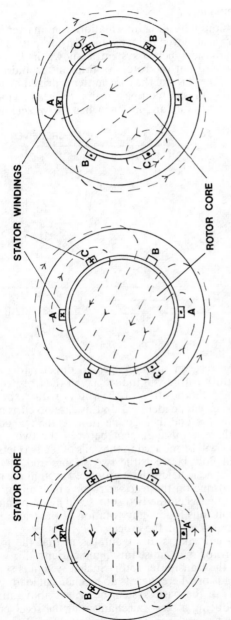

Fig. A.6   Rotation of magnetic field in three phase stator windings.

Synchro Transmission

The transmission of heading information from master compass to distant repeaters is achieved in many modern compasses by synchro transmission. A basic synchro system is shown in figure A.7. No amplification is used but the rotors of transmitter and receiver are energised by a.c. The rotor of the transmitter is driven by mechanical gearing from the master compass azimuth gear, which rotates relative to the vessel's fore and aft line when the vessel alters course.

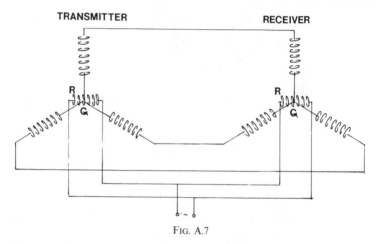

FIG. A.7

The rotor in the receiver motor is geared directly to the repeater compass card. Both rotors will induce a.c. in their respective stator windings which, if the position of the rotors with respect to their stators is the same, will be identical. In this case no current will flow in the stator windings and their connections as the two components will cancel. If there is misalignment between the two rotors, then different voltages will be induced in the coils of the two sets of stators and current will flow between the two stators and in the stators themselves. A magnetic field will be produced around the stator coils which exerts a torque on the receiver rotor which aligns itself until no torque is exerted when the two rotors will again be aligned. The receiver rotor will thus follow any rotation of the transmitter rotor turning the repeater card in the process.

This basic system suffers disadvantages in that the load on the receiver motor rotor may cause misalignment and this will cause a torque back on the transmitter rotor. Such a system is suitable only for very light loads or where there is no mechanical load.

The problems of the basic system described above may be prevented by introducing a servo mechanism at the receiver end. The receiver rotor then merely provides an electrical signal which controls

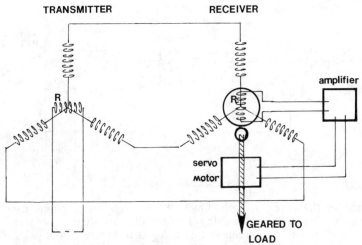

FIG. A.8

the servo mechanism which performs the work of moving the load. Such a system is shown in figure A.8.

The rotor of the transmitter is fed with a.c. and is driven by the master compass azimuth gear. Currents are induced in the stator windings of the transmitter, and identical currents must therefore flow in the stator windings of the receiver. Unless the receiver rotor is aligned in its required position an a.c. will be induced in it by the alternating magnetic field around the stator coils. This signal is amplified and used to drive the servo motor which is mechanically geared to the rotor to turn it to seek the null position where the signal induced in the rotor is zero. This will occur when the rotor is aligned at right angles to the resultant magnetic field of the stator coils. Any rotation of this field caused by a rotation of the transmitter rotor will therefore cause a corresponding rotation of the receiver rotor. The servo motor in the receiver may be geared also to the mechanical load which in the case of a gyro transmission system may be the transmitter rotor of a step by step motor which serves several repeaters. As the work is done by the servo motor whose power is derived from the amplifier power supply, no load is placed on the receiver rotor enabling the load to be transmitted back to the transmitter. A large number of repeaters may be served in this way.

Many modern compass installations provide power to move the load of the repeater cards by using the signals induced in the transmitter stator windings to control switching amplifier circuits which themselves control the currents flowing in the receiver stator coils. As the transmitter rotor turns the coils in the receiver are switched in turn to produce a corresponding rotation of the magnetic

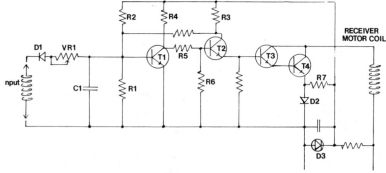

Fig. A.9   Switching amplifier circuit.

field in the receiver, with which the receiver rotor aligns itself. Figure A.9 shows the switching circuit of such a system.

The input to the circuit in figure A.9 is from one of the pairs of coils in an inductive transmitter (see compass S.R. 120, section 2.22). There will be one such circuit for each pair of transmitter coils, each circuit serving one pair of coils in the receiver motor.

The a.c. input is applied to the base of transistor T1 via R1, VR1 and diode D1, which rectifies to produce a negative going half wave rectified current. In the absence of this input T1 is forward biased by current flowing through R2 and R3. A collector-emitter current flows through R4 causing T1 collector to go positive. This potential is divided by R5 and R6 and is applied to the base of T2. This reverse biases T2 which therefore does not conduct. In this state T3 and T4 are reversed biased as the base of T3 goes negative relative to the emitter, whose potential is raised by current flowing through R7 and D2 when T2 is off. In the absence of any collector current through T4 the coil in the receiver is not energised from the supply.

An increase in a.c. voltage input flows through R1, VR1 and D1 as a half wave rectified negative current, which charges C1 to the potential across R1. This makes the base of T1 negative and T1 is reverse biased. Collector current ceases and collector potential rises, and also the base potential of T2, which is then forward biased. T2 collector current flows forward biasing T3 and T4. The collector emitter current of T4 flows through the receiver motor coils from the supply thus energising the coils.

D3 is a voltage regulating zener diode. The variable resistor VR1 is adjusted such that the on/off intervals are equal as required (see section 2.22).

INDEX

A

'A' bracket   67, 70, 79
Acceleration   xii
Alternating current   133
  generation of   134
Amplifier, follow up   72, 86, 108, 125, 142
  transmission   79, 92
Anchutz compass   44, 118
  standards 3 and 4   118
  standard 6   127
  standard 10   130
Angular acceleration   xiv
  momentum   xix, 2, 4
  velocity   xiii, 3
Arma Brown compass   52, 62, 64, 101
Azimuth   4
  gear   69
  motor   69, 72

B

Ballistic   32
  deflection   52, 59, 62
  liquid   32
  tilt   63
Bearing   4
  calculation of   17
Binnacle   74, 85
Bottom heavy control   26, 124

C

Cager   98
Calculation of bearing   17
  on PZX triangle   12
Compass card assembly   74
Control   24
  ellipse   29
    period of   36
  pots   32
  precession   26, 29
  weight   25
Correction of errors   74, 86, 110, 127
  of rolling error   127
  torque motor   75, 77

Cosine resolver   75
Couple   xvi, 22
Course and speed error   48
  change in   52, 60
  correction of   75, 111
  formula for   51

D

Damping   36
  error   42, 47, 74, 110
  factor   41
  in azimuth   42
  in tilt   36
  precession   38
  weight   37, 70, 84
Declination   6
Directional gyro   64, 113
Drifting   4
  formula for   9

E

Earth, rotation of   1, 4, 5
Electrolytic level   98
Errors   47
  acceleration (see rolling errors)
  change in speed   52
  correction of   74, 86, 110, 127
  course and speed   48
  damping   42, 47, 74, 110
  latitude (see damping)
  rolling   52
E shaped transformer   71, 109

F

Follow up   70, 85, 106, 124
Force, unit of   xii
Fluorolube   104
Free gyroscope   1
Frequency   133

G

Generator   134
Gimbal, azimuth   104

Gimbal—*contd.*
  primary 102
  tilt 104
Graphite domes 126, 129
Gravitation xii
Gravitational constant xiii
Gravity control 24
Gyration, radius of xviii
Gyro, directional 64, 113
  free 1
  star 4
  three degrees of freedom 1
  twin arrangement 122
Gyro ball 101
Gyroscope, free 1
Gyroscopic inertia 2
Gyrospheret 93, 118, 128

H

Hertz 133

I

Induction motor 135
Inductive transmitter 87
Inertia xiii
  gyroscopic 2
Intercardinal rolling error 54
  elimination of 57, 62

K

Kilogramme xi

L

Latitude error (see damping error)
Length, unit of xi
Levelling, automatic 99
Liquid ballistic 32
Lubber line 72, 86

M

Mass, unit of xi
Metre, definition of xi
Moment xv
  of inertia xvii, 3
Momentum xiii
  angular xix, 2, 4
Motor, induction 135
  step by step 113

N

Newton xii
Nominal vertical axis 70

O

Outer member 69
  sphere 118, 129

P

Peak voltage 133
Pendulum unit 108
Period of control ellipse 36
  schuler 62
Phantom element 69, 84
  yoke 98
Precession 22
  control 38
  damping 38, 44
  rate of 24, 34
Primary gimbal 102
PZX triangle 12

R

Radian xiii
Radius of gyration xvii
Repulsion coil 118, 128
Rigidity in space (see Gyroscopic inertia)
Rolling errors 32, 52, 54
  elimination of 57, 62, 127

S

Schuler period 62
  tuning 62
Second, definition of xi
Sensitive element 66, 79, 93, 101, 118
Settling error (see damping error)
Settling position 41, 42, 46, 47
Sidereal day 5
S.I. units xi
Sperry compasses 66
  Mk. 20 52, 54, 62, 66, 84
  SR/120/130 79
  Mk. 37 93
Spider element 120
Spin, direction of 26
Spinners 101
Stationary element 84
Steaming error (see course and speed
  error)
Steam bearings 69
Step by step motor 113
Support frame 67
Suspension 67, 70, 79
Synchro transmitter 78, 111, 117, 140

T

Tank, follow up   104
Three phase supplies   135, 137
Tilt   4
Tilting   4
  formula for   10
Time, unit of   xi
Top heavy control   25
Torque   xvi, 22
Torsion wires   101, 103, 106
Transmission to repeaters   78, 87, 113
Transmitter, synchro   78, 111, 117, 140
Two phase supplies   135

U

Units, S.I.   xi

V

Velocity   xii
Vertical axis   1, 37, 68
  false   53, 58
  ring   66, 79

W

Weight   xii
  control   25
  damping   37, 70, 84
Wires suspension   67, 70, 79

Z

Zenith   5